ABELARD

ABELARD

CEDRIC WHITMAN

HARVARD UNIVERSITY PRESS

CAMBRIDGE · MASSACHUSETTS

1965

Distributed in Great Britain by Oxford University Press, London

Library of Congress Catalog Card Number 65-22057

Printed in the United States of America

ABELARD

I

A man was waiting in the dark alone,
Night wind tumultuous with pontifical
Thunder and promise of a dawn to come.
Above his head, a pyramid of shadow,
Notre Dame nudged toward God, but not as yet
In heaven silver vestige, but thin rain.
Alone he waited, and the dawn began.

A lantern swung uncertainly in gust
And drip at the street's angle; from behind it
A footstep and a pious protestation
Blew across mud and cobblestones.
                                    "Thibault?"
The young man called. Over the lantern spoke
A hooded face, a bored voice:
                        "March is the month
Cain killed his brother, and for all my vows,
I hardly blame him."

                        Out of the dark Thibault
Came spattered and sardonic: "Do we sing
Matins the night before, so monks can sleep
And save their eyes for pricked illuminings
Of spiderweb minuscule, just to be

Routed at rooster time by some birdheaded
Pretender to the throne of Aristotle?
O you philosophers! No charity,
No Christian understanding! You pursue
Pagan beasts, you and your wisdom, wizards
That peep and mutter after universals!
Thereafter come the whores of Babylon."

He stamped the moisture from his feet, and sighed:
"Save your own soul, I am no missionary;
I am a scribe. But why do you waylay
Your idol like a brigand in the dark?"

The boy laughed, brushing rain out of his eyes:
"Brother Thibault, the world is new alive.
Sloth will not plough by reason of the cold,
And sluggards cry of lions in the streets.
Who loves his soul, arising early, plucks
His lute for wisdom's freshly opening eyes,
Hoping a loosehaired and ungirdled vision
At the mind's tower window. Is it true,
As learned gossip goes, that Anselm's flock
Has left its master to hear Abelard?"

"These dust storms blow by me," Thibault replied.
The rain was stopping, and a lifting sky
Painted bright house tops, and invented trees
Along the Seine bank. Notre Dame revealed
Her stiffened saints and heavy portals. Windows
Burned candles, and the day's first hawker cried.

Toward the old palace a hot courier
Galloped his mission's end. A fishwife cuffed
A thieving gamin. In a high cold attic
A gaunt-eyed scholar took his fasting pen.
The wind from eastward quarters of the sun
Blew harder, blew the boy's hair round his face,
And blew out the monk's lantern. Thibault grunted:

"There now, my light is gone."
                              "The sun is up,"
The boy said; "Abelard is coming now."

Ruddy aloft barbaric festivals
Arose, torn cloud in gold spasms of dawn
Scalded the pallid sky, majestically
Casting up arch on arch, and the great sun
Fountained up long arms into heaven. Round
The corner of the church came Abelard
Alone on his way to Mt. Ste. Geneviève,
And Thibault called and stopped him:
                                    "Abelard,
Master of those who someday hope to know!
What do you teach so early?"
                            "Early tasks,"
Said Abelard. "Young heads at the Cathedral,
Pondering the trivium in double dark,
Plod pencils and plan slingshots. Why do you
Greet me here like a Roman consul?"
                                  "Not,"
Said Thibault, making wrinkles in his nose,

3

"From lust for finely minced philosophy.
You have no faith, you are a heretic.
I think that you are charted for damnation
Full sailed with vanity and mortal pride."

Abelard laughed aloud: "Your ghouls and goblins
Have glimmered damply round my door for years!
You rise at dawn to tell me this?"
                                        Thibault
Fluttered one hand: "Blame this young cannibal,
Eager to eat you up, books pens and mildew.
Have you a famulus? If not, I vouch
He speaks Latin, can count, and will not steal."

"How do you know?" said Abelard.
                                        Thibault
Cried squinting: "There! No word suffices you,
Not friend's nor priest's! Evidence, evidence!
Here, Didymus, shove your curious finger, pry!
His father was an old Italian friend
I knew on pilgrimage."
                                Abelard turned
His eyes on the young man: "Have you a name?"

He shook his head saying: "My name is Empty;
Fill me. I have been listening and caught flying
Your words on each wind blowing south. Desire
Behind closed doors builds its necessity
Before the mind has keys. You have the keys
To open me and let my Easter in,

You, the almighty Caesar of all minds
Alive. Take me for tribune to your will,
And I will earn the name Antonius."

Abelard smiled: "You lack no rhetoric,
Antonius. How children fly at love
And burgeon into eloquence! But love
Strikes bitter, and less timely than the spring.
Behind closed doors . . . And when the doors
                                        are split,
Not Easter, but Good Friday marches in."
He frowned: "See boy, a famulus lives hard,
Reads long, trots far, eats little, and gets kicked.
You like it?"

        And Antoine: "Good Friday first,
Easter when God wills."

          Abelard looked pale
As the sun made his eyes droop wearily:
"Perhaps you are less ignorant than I.
Thibault, what a good friend you are, to scold
My ways, to shield my hope of grace, and now
To bring this subtle sage who begs for knowledge."

"He might be your salvation," said Thibault.
"Take him. I go, though the sun ramps too high
For sleep, and I too far asleep to write.
I shall sit nodding at my desk all day
Misreading nimium for minimum,
And bark at all the brothers."

                    Abelard
Called after him: "Visit my logic class,
Thibault; I'll prove to you there is no reason
Why sleepy men should bark. Sleep shrinks
                        the brain,
Antoine," he turned severely on the boy;
"If you have slept this night, as I have not,
You will not comprehend one enthymeme
Of all I say. Come, listen. Beware sleep."

They climbed the street stair to Mt. Ste. Geneviève,
Into the raftered high hospitium,
Where Antoine found a bench to be his own.
Outside, the gliding sun rode easily
On brimming panes and shot white squares and
                        rhomboids
To blazon order on a hush of scholars.
Abelard climbed the lectern, and offhand
Flicking the Organon, page after page,
Not glancing at his listeners, said:
                        "Forms
Exist, as I have proved, upon the mind's
Ocean, but not as flotsam, fallen or flung,
Broken from the substance of dry land or ship,
But as the regularity of swells,
Part of the sea. Aristotle declares:
'Knowledge demonstrable cannot exist
Of inessential accidents.' "
                        He paused,

And flicked the pages of the Organon:
"Must I accept form as an accident
I cannot demonstrate? Not if I know
All trees are trees, and Socrates himself
And Abelard, though one great and one small,
Both men, whatever that foretells. Consider,
What have we? Legs, arms, belly, difference
And sameness, heads with wisdom or without.
But he is dead and I am still alive,
And he was ugly, I, they say, less ugly,
And he was wise, and I am in the dark.
How should we stamp upon our differences
One human franchise? Somewhere in God's mind
The shape we know by his invented reason
Rises and falls and foams white, evident.
Sea calls to sea, and spindrift knowledge writes
Patterns of light on our chaotic dark;
Our surface is a filigree, like silver
Scrolled over glass. But once, three primal shapes,
Cube, circle, triangle were born of space,
And out of these . . ."

His voice ran on, but half
Preoccupied. Two faces in the room,
A heavy face and a light placid face,
Gazed upward listening, blunting as they gazed
The scalpels of epistemology.
How could they bring such faces to his high
Hospitium of minds, where processes
And functions were unrolled? Here triple arched

The glory of the Trinity, framed cold
In mighty exegesis stood explained,
And the hot contests of the last Redemption
Flamed in the naked abstract, all for minds.
He looked away, but they pursued his eye,
One heavy and one light, the heavy face
A crater of responses to each word.
Mount Aetna comes upon us, Abelard
Thought, and his voice broke through his ears,
                                      saying:
"Mount Aetna comes upon us; put it so:
If forms drop random rooted nowhere, why
Might not the universal mountain Aetna
Dump itself on our heads, puffing pumice
And lava, banging its obsidian
Rock passions round us, a Typhoeus loose
To blast our temperate voiced philosophies?
We feed in peril of particulars
If universals gad so free of them!
No, keep self's earthen moment for our safety,
And this roof will remain both name and knowledge.
But lose the name, the species and the self,
And we must cease to be philosophers,
And may as well turn birds and fly away,
Or crime laden, a bestial sacrifice,
Dive in the fiery crater and be lost."

He closed the book and applause beat the roof.
The heavy face was smiling. Abelard

8

Stepped down and greeted it:
>   "Canon Fulbert,
> You graze upon my words too carefully.
> You will discover quicksands."

>   Fulbert puffed
> A little through his nose: "Quicksands in you?
> You are all polished granite, fame deserved
> And ripe for greater fame, if such there is.
> From pure delight I squirmed like a hooked fish.
> Mount Aetna — what nimble complexity!
> What made you think of Aetna?"

>   Abelard
> Answered: "Sometimes distinguished visitors
> Tempt my tongue into image."

>   Solemnly
> And carefully he sought the other face;
> Teacher, philosopher, looked down to where
> She turned her eyes up.

>   "And does Heloise
> Now rise so early to attend in hall
> Redoubtable doctors, in the wilds of reason,
> Stalking the print and spoor of fleeting proof?
> Woman, I thought, pursued surefooted fact."

> Fulbert put his great arm round Heloise:
> "My niece belies her womanhood. She is
> More at home with her brain than with her instinct.
> Daily she sits at books I cannot read,
> And pries up heavy doctrine from the bedded

Hardpan of holy pages. Mysteries
Melt at her scrutiny. What can be done,
What can be done with such a prodigy,
Unless God rigs a special galleon
To float her destiny?"

                              Abelard, gazing
At Heloise: "Are you so studious?"

"I read a little," answered Heloise,
And her voice was a woman, rounder than
Her body's girl. Fulbert puffed:

                              "Diffident";
He winked and stroked her hair, and she placidly
Expressionless leaned from his touch a little:
"I say if half your scholars showed the zeal
She burns with, ours would be a blessed time.
She ought to have a tutor."

                              Abelard
Stood waiting with a cold smile on his lips.
All three were staring at the floor, but he
Was staring down the cliff. To fly, to fly
Is beautiful, but wingless to leap down,
Despair and death. He waited for the word
And knew that it was coming, a word planned
By a long indirection, courtierlike,
After one vision of her. Innocently
He waited in his academic hall,
And the volcanic Titan was awake,
The blast of the earthborn breath over the bright hill

Came scorching to the cliff's edge where they hung.

"She ought to have a tutor," said Fulbert.
"And yet, I must be cautious too; a man
Of continence, no doubt, not to abuse
My trust. But learned too. He must be learned.
And he would live with us, more fortunate
Than some philosophers, living on quails
And quince."
                    Fulbert, hand resting heavily
On Heloise's shoulder, smiled and shook
His head: "I wonder, is there anyone?
What of you, Canon Abelard? What of you?"

And the ground tilted, the air yawned below.
A world of prinking courtiers, easy skill
Harnessing easy ignorance, all dropped
Hooded with blind desire down the abyss.
Abelard raised hot eyes of pitying hate,
And Fulbert's fell. Then, like a river fingering
And lipping a long blade of margin ice,
Abelard said:
                    "My labors are not light.
My hours are nailed to tasks. My brain is shrunk
With sleeplessness."
                    Glowering, Fulbert cried:
"But who is left? The world of thought is you,
All others rinds and rubbish."
                    Abelard

Answered: "I know an old man, very wise,
Not famed, but marveled for his continence.
If God still spares him, he would teach your niece."

Fulbert said: "Good, rake wisdom from the grave."
But Abelard stood bleak. No tremor's breath
Stirred the long fluted pillar of his gown.
He answered nothing, and Fulbert recovering:
"I looked, of course, for your new subtleties,
But they are not for women. Well, do not
Hasten to fetch that old man. I must think,
And wonder if in canons of one church
Trust, obligation, gracious interchange . . ."

But Abelard, turning his eyes away:
"I mean only her good. She is still young.
You may confuse your judgment with devotion
In thrusting her upon philosophy
In years when the brook leaps and saplings dance."

Heloise kept her eyes low, and Fulbert,
Now with his hand cradling around her arm,
Bowed silently, and drew her after him.
But Heloise smiled backward from the door,
And left in the empty doorway a light smile.

Antoine came forward. "Master," he said. Violently
Abelard whirled:
                    "To the far end of hell!"

He shouted, and as Antoine sped away,
Called after him: "Early you witness, boy,
The cracked mirror. Come back. God sent you here.
You saw that man? Run after him, and say
That Master Abelard, half ill with toil,
Will ask his pardon at another time
For roughshod words."
                              Gently he pushed him on.
Under the lintel hung her beckoning smile.

II

The smile tarried and called. Beyond, Paris
Danced to the ringing of the day's bright anvils;
On every roof the hammers of the sun
Fell flaming, on the baldly shining head
Of every tree; sparks charged the compass points
And floated burning on the silver Seine.
The wild and crooked grace flowed every way,
Dancing in the streets crazily, and weaving
A flickering siege around the hill of peace.
Abelard shook his head, murmuring:

"Dance

Dance, gold over green, as once the halcyon
Ghost spent himself through his creative, brooding
Hands on the new made waters, hallowing
Green earthliness and banners of the sun!
The angel of a deathless heresy
Fingers my throat. We doctors have translated
Trees into faith's bare artifact, while dancers
Dance; and if they could reason, they would all
Be heretics, who in simplicity
Of mindless rhythm crowd confessionals
Moaning, I love a woman. Yet they know
Something unknown to me, who can outscold
The fangless coils of logic, sacred snake.

There is a dangerousness about a man
That wants danger. I gave my lands away
To dig God's cold and perfect diamond,
Chiseled all round, white fire that needs no light
To shine. The sun disgraces me, three days
My senior brother, who ignites the colored
Facets of the earth's jewels, all my elders,
Till now shimmering hovers a light smile
Before the open doorways of the mind . . .
Rose without thorn, pray for all those in darkness."

There without thorn she stood upon the moon,
Her hands balanced in prayer upon her breast,
And face of Heloise. Abelard sighed:

"Thorns prod my skin. I sowed them there myself,
Contriving her my pupil, smile and thorn.
And this great Aetna, has he not perceived
What premise warps my square of inference?
She smiles and the door dances on its post.
But now too late. Fulbert is angry now.
Coward ambition shrank away goosefleshed.
It is too late. My diamond waits for me."

He turned and opening a narrow portal
Entered the smell of books, his escritoire.
He collared Abelard, and sat him down
Before the table where long arguments
Debates and challenges lay written out
For answer. But the mirror misted, reason's

Accustomed sunbeam slumbered on the glass.
Abelard gazed through words and paper down
To grainy wood, to forests of tall timber
Where wood was born, wet, green, and solacing,
Forests, where men were sometimes slain alone
And buried leafily for spring to find
Fleshless, the white geometry of men;
Forests, green mortal highways of desire
Where death is true. The best have died, Plato
And Romulus, with few tears . . . though some die
And are bewailed, as on the red field David
Wept lyric sorrow over Jonathan,
David the slinger and Goliath slayer,
David the laughing and magnanimous harper
Harping for Saul, David the soul and flesh
Of a rhapsodic earth, lifting its hands;
David by the side of slain Jonathan, mourning,
Bitten by the dark fangs deeply, singing still . . .

When Abelard then saw what he had written,
Surprise first shook him; this for Jonathan?
"Or myself lie beside you here . . ." He thought,
"Here is my madness born. My half heaven falls.
I gaze upon myself and am not grieved,
But weary, fascinated by the heavy dance,
That dark thump-treading of the streets down there.
Even here, we are not free . . . Jonathan . . ."

From the scholar's hill went Abelard, and across a
                                    glaring angle

Of the city. But the sun was veiled, the cloud of afternoon
Made the dance gray, and everywhere its joy was hidden.
Under his feet the still hot dust held up a desert mouth,
And two half naked urchins, illuvial human fragments,
Rolled in it, fighting silently. Abelard went his way,
And coming under the prickly vast shadow of Notre Dame,
Stepped into the stone heart of the shadow. Two novice
                     priests, his pupils,
Bowed to him hopefully, but he passed, seeking the
                     tower stairs,
And there he climbed, spiraling upward like a
                     wingless eagle,
By bronze bells clustering and hovering under the
                     dusty rafters
Halfway to the moon, reserving their terrible rapture
On this, no special day, with silent lolling tongues;
To a high belfry at last, where the sky came in,
To a platform of stone, whereunder scrawled flat in
                     the dust
Paris lay, and the gentle plains to north and east,
The brown woods shining no longer in the
                     aging afternoon,
And fifty miles of the river going like a snake.
    Abelard breathed and stepped out on the belfry.

    And there a gargoyle carved in stone sat grimly
        Gazing over the belfry rim.
    He seemed to laugh. His mouth was frozen wide,
        And eyes in his forehead numbering three
        Saw somewhat more than some men see.

Four ears grew from either side,
And round him sprang in spidery tangles
Legs at incalculable angles,
Mocking the ordered choir and stately organ
With the stone grimace of a gorgon.
There he sat his perilous perch,
Frightening demons from the church.

"Ah," said the beast, "now Mass is sung,
Let us converse in the vulgar tongue.
Few ever come to talk with me,
Because of my vulgarity."

"I have an idea," said Abelard,
"That you and I are both ill starred;
You fixed on an outside limb of the spire,
I shut in, a mouse in the choir,
Neither initiate to tell
Where the roads part for Heaven and Hell."

The gargoyle laughed with a swampy croak:
"Come now, you know it's all a joke,
Those kicks and clouts laid up below
For the things you did, or almost did,
And didn't confess till time to go,
So some got caught in the coffin lid
And botched your chances at the gate,
And the angel smirked, Too late, too late.
No, here I watch both world and sea
As if it happened all for me.

As for inside, I hear their stuff
Nine times a day, and that's enough."

Abelard laughed: "The bishop would glower
If he knew such a heathen sat on his tower."

The gargoyle glared with a cynical sneer:
"Let the bishop recall, he put me here."

"The bishop put you there, my friend,
To serve a holy and pious end."

"My end is fine. It is made of stone,
And better than yours of beef and bone,"
The gargoyle snapped. "Did you come here
To read off sermons in my ear,
Or listen, and learn a song or two
That I might have to sing to you?"

Abelard leaned on the belfry rim:
"Garrulous gargoyle, lewd and grim,
Speak!"
          And the stone unflinching smile
Answered softly: "Patience a while.
Grandly I sing when I am wet,
And rain is coming. Vapors fret
The sky, but when the full rain falls
I spout my wisdom down the walls."

Over the gleaming last of day
A single cloud of battered gray

Sowed rumbling fire and rain like seeds
On apse and chimney, river and reeds;
As rain roared in his rainpipe throat,
The gargoyle raised a guttural note;
Glib with his wet voice after drouth,
As the bubbles came dribbling out of his mouth,
He blew them free from the end of his snout,
And watched them sally, watched them fall,
And rally in streams as they brushed the wall;
And seeing them dropping, spinning about,
He gurgled in rain his whole song out:

"Praise God in muscle and bone, praise God
Of the hungry glebe and thirsty sod.
Praise God who glimmers in the seams
Of sunset hill and trilling streams.
Praise happy God who dwells below
In root and grass and water flow.
I am His gargoyle, elegant thing,
Rare, extempore, hear me sing,
How God winked and laid Him asleep
While a muddy gargoyle crawled from the deep;
Gremlin gargoyle, sleek and slick,
A bottom of stone on a base of brick;
Graceful gargoyle, whose high mass
Is wind over the clovered grass.
My stony throat is a waterway
Of wonderful hymns for a rainy day.
And the shadow under my rocky wing
Will baffle your eyes with ecstasy.

None resist when they hear me sing
My doggerel canticle, carol and glee
Of gullible girdles, girls and glances,
Puddles of rain that search the sky
In shimmer and flash, when thumping dances
Pound the ground and Osannas sound,
Kindling that great lascivious Eye
So loved the world it chose to die
For cradle and corn, for mothers singing,
For trapped flies buzzing, mules in mire,
Souls in sackcloth, flesh in fire.
Hurrah for God of the great desire!
Hurrah for the angel He sent winging!
Hurrah for the gargoyle on His spire!"

The rain ceased and the song ceased,
And silence fell upon the beast.
Abelard quietly smiled to think
What consternation might be stirred
If the good bishop could have heard
His gargoyle's metaphysic of sink
And gutter flinging high and clear
From the saintly spire for the world to hear.
And slowly, with the belfry's calm
Blue vista lengthening his gaze,
He left the tower of Notre Dame,
And walked through a slaked city, where the day's
Last arrows, flying through the shattered cloud,
Struck in the rain wet target of the dusk,
And drove earth huddling eastward into darkness.

III

Abelard, twisting from the roasted quail,
Fingered a nubbed and jeweled goblet. Smiles
Drove his eyes haunting into corners, ghosts
Before the cock. Gold, not of plate or cup,
Gold, scattering radiance down placid shoulders,
Gleamed close at his left hand. He gazed away.
Fulbert said smiling:
     "March was a cold time
To tempt you. Summer lifts a kindlier eye.
Austere old Cato's self chewed cake in summer,
And retched at Roman cabbage."
          Abelard
Scowled quickly back: "Losing austerity
I lose myself."
      But Fulbert said: "In you
Self is abundant. You may spend it freely —
Today's great man, tomorrow's history,
A frost that cracks the pillars of the schools,
A sun that burns their roofs transparent. Rule
Therefore, Abelard, with long earned liberty,
You, so famed for continence! To whom else
Could I entrust my jewel? Your shame-tattered
Rivals cry you heretic, pagan, even

Beelzebub; but chaste."

Abelard's brow
Bent volleying shafts of anger. Heloise
Gazed at her hands, and Fulbert helplessly
Shrank in his chair. Then Abelard laughed, saying:

"If chastity be virtue, praise the God
Who saved me from temptation! In the years
Men dream of kisses, learning held me hard.
I never saw a face or fall of hair
Lovelier than metaphysic. Fool was what
They called me then; the sandals on my stair
Were Plato's. Out of ignorance of lust
I failed to theorize of chastity,
For never till tonight has woman sat
So close to me. And now, Philosophy,
For twenty years my only mistress, here
Suborns me to the courts of woman, leading
One who stares at the sun of heavenly reason,
Careless of natural gold. Perhaps, perhaps,
Logic's incarnate muse pursues me, made
In woman's likeness, to complete that myth
And scholar's dream, which you call chastity."

Heloise smiled, and Fulbert bending forward:
"No, you must be the master. Heloise
Is no incarnate muse, but she can learn.
Her face is good enough; but, unto her
That hath, as Scripture says! God gave her also
Brain, and your goodness undertakes His will.

2 3

I am too old, or I would sit with you
And sponge up wisdom. No, my duty ends
When you have made our child a new Hypatia."

He rose. Abelard rising also answered:
"Heaven keep her safe! Hypatia ended badly,
And under churchly hands. Behold what harm
Religion does, the poet said; and he,
Fulbert, was epicurean, yet austere,
Lover of death, lust hater, yearning past
Life's superstitious ritual of self love
Toward innocence, a dead child, sacrificed . . .
Your omen of Hypatia frightens me.
Let her sleep, passion ended, in her grave."

Fulbert reached out and caught Abelard's sleeve:
"How easily I scratch you, meaning praise!"

Abelard said: "But I deserve no praise."

Fulbert said: "Yet allow my joy; in hope
And praise of youth, age mends itself. But I
Shall keep apart; find omens where you will.
Goodnight. Forgive my rasping years."
                                        He bowed,
And Abelard the first time stood alone
With Heloise. In pulseless candlelight
Staining a silence trackless yet of word,
She waited by the window looking out
At the warm summer night. He watched the curved

Falling of flamelit hair along her shoulder,
As mercilessly helpless without fear
She waited, gathering from the wide window
The strong nurturing of the night upon her.
Like Parian stone she stood inevitable,
Singular, set apart for wonder, closed
In ceremonies of the candled air.
And Abelard said:
                    "It is late. My eyes
Are shimmering from staring down the secrets
Of gold illuminated manuscripts.
My ears ring with lament. Perhaps I hear
Hypatia's ghost, disconsolate among
These windy summer leaves she lost too soon.
Now she goes circling with the zodiac.
Was it her quest of wisdom, or is death
Alone enough to mask the summer night
With the pale features of a drifting wraith?"

Heloise smiled a little, murmuring, "Death
And wisdom; which will ours be?"
                                    Abelard
Answered: "They have been walking hand in hand
So long we must be shrewd to catch them singly.
Our task is reason, but the hour is late
For a beginning."
                    And he turned away,
And roamed abroad in the dark leafiness,
Far fragrance of exhaustless, delicate
Wind wrapping him away from candle gleam's

Immediate gold, toward deep neutralities
Of night, few paces, but afar. He paused:
A white ghost in the street ahead of him
Dewily glimmering, a cloaked woman,
Walked or danced, grave gestures summoning,
Beckoning him to his own house on the hill.
He followed slowly, softly calling her:
"Who are you?"

     The ghost turned; her face was veiled,
And in a wailing voice: "I am Wisdom.
You sought me. Will you now forget me? Come,
Come home."

    And Abelard: "Veiled and unseen,
Not to be trusted. Wisdom has clear eyes.
Let me pass."

     But the voice cried: "I am yours!
Unknown you must receive me. Come, come home."
"Which way?" said Abelard. The voice was still,
And the ghost wrung pale hands perplexedly.
Abelard left it glimmering there, and passed
A lane of trees to a Cistercian cell.
Thibault was by his lamp:

      "You walk by night
Communing with black spirits, Abelard.
When will you leave these philosophic wars
And sleep on the full belly of true faith?
You look well."

    "I am ill," said Abelard.
He sat braiding his fingers thoughtfully.

Thibault gazed at him.

           "And is this," he said,
"Formidable Abelard the rationalist,
The Demogorgon of the yeas and nays?
Are such men ever ill? Do earthly laurels
Wither, old friend, while always flourishing
Time ramps and leaves you older? On the grave
Of reason does the final angel weep
For one who tried conclusions with his God?"

Abelard shrugged impatiently and said:
"What are you talking of, Thibault? Tonight
True faith has made me ill. I am in haste.
Someone is waiting in the street for me.
How can a man love God? I always thought
Anything I could argue for myself
Was not the business of the busy Lord.
And yet, how busy is the Lord, Thibault?
Does He not sometimes, bored with heaven, hurl
Earthquakes and avalanches at our lives
For high diversion?"

           "Bravo!" cried Thibault.
"There, Abelard. You feel much better now.
Blasphemous Manichee, can you stand up
In Notre Dame and lecture Christian boys?
What avalanche has ever struck your life,
The pampered peacock of the schools? No, Peter,
Faith is not yet your illness. You have still
To sicken more. I cannot talk with you."

And Abelard: "Someone is waiting for me,
While you avoid the question."
                              And Thibault:
"There is no question. How is Antonius?"

"Alone," said Abelard. "No, not ejected.
He keeps my house alone. And where am I?
I came to ask you that. I seem to dwell
At Canon Fulbert's house, tutor and friend
To Heloise, his niece. I thought I lived
In cities built on hills of intellect.
I live in Africa. There is, besides,
A gargoyle on the tower of Notre Dame
Who hates the bishop and sings doggerel.
Nothing is worse than to believe in things.
Do not believe in me. Yet Heloise
Speaks dainty Latin. She is summerlike,
And if her uncle tells the truth, she knows
The bulgy books of learning . . ."
                              Abelard
Stopped short before Thibault's face. There
                              was silence.
Then gently Thibault:
                    "You, Abelard? You?"

"I think that it is I," said Abelard.
"I ask you too."
                "It might be you," Thibault
Said in slow mockery. "Peacock, as I said.
You are fine featured. You are not a priest.

You never had true faith. Why should I care
If now you lose your reason?"
                    Abelard
Shook himself, laughing strangely: "What a place
You live in! Come and walk under the leaves!
Come out, Thibault, and be old friends again!
Faith is alive. You sit wizened, weathering
The fireshod storms of sin and penitence —
How can you sin in here? Come sin with faith,
Come out with me."
                    "Ropedancer," said Thibault.
"You toss your words like colored balls for mobs.
Mountebank talk. I cannot mend you."
                              "No,"
Said Abelard, "I knew that you could not."

He went out, calmly passing up the lane
As if a star had settled on his shoulder.
The ghost was by the tree.
                    "I know you now,"
He said to it. "Let us go where you go."

The ghost unveiled the face of Heloise
And led him past the river, through the soft
Articulate darkness home to Fulbert's house.

But when the morning washed with a firm light
An upstairs room of oak and tapestry,
Abelard called his pupil, and she sat
Silently in the window seat, her hands

29

Linked in her lap, and waited. Memories
Began to blot prefashioned words. He said:
"You came to school three times, but never asked
A question."
                    Heloise said: "Fearing laughter,
I let hard words and puzzlement go by.
But once I almost asked. May I ask now?
Is logic our divinest function? Yes,
Plato said that, but what of Abelard?"

He raised his brows. "Plato and Abelard
For once agree. If you deny, your dreams
And studies will be one. Logic alone
Has reared theology from cradle songs
To long-robed hymns and given her a crown.
All science hangs from Aristotle's square.
Do you doubt this?"
                    "To learn and to believe
Are mine," she said. "My doubts and dreams
                                        are one."

"Reason is a firm light," said Abelard
With old habitual severity;
"For God Himself reasoned His whole design,
And all things yield, all human things, to reason."

"Sometimes," said Heloise, "I think I know
Unreasoned truth. But guesses are not knowledge.
And first, if you would tell what knowledge is,
And say if it is being or a name — "

30

"A name," said Abelard. "Enough of old
De Champeaux's bodiless realities.
Why do you fly at questions so far flung,
Not yet convinced of reason?"
                                        Heloise
Lowered her eyes: "I am ashamed. Forgive
My readiness to doubt. Show me the way
That I must think."
                        He said: "There is no way
Save dialectic, Aristotle's bones;
But you must make the flesh of argument,
Find your own way, and then forget your masters."

Heloise looked at him: "Am I so free?
Shall I forget you then?"
                            And Abelard:
"If I teach you as little as my masters
Taught me, forget me soon."
                                "Begin," she said,
And folding quietly the wings of will,
Sat attentive. Abelard, his mind veering
Like sloops in flaw, but with a weighty look,
    First opened, and then closed a book.
    He paced a little up and down,
    And then said with an earnest frown:
    "First let me show you reason: mark
    The limbs of logic, how they bind
    To cogent crosses every lark
    And lilting of the wandering mind.
    For proof, only observe these few

Syllogisms; for God and you
And I are syllogisms too;
Nor need we speak of A's and B's,
Of triangles and Socrates;
No, let us take the things we know
Ourselves to be, and prove them so.
Let me mold premises, whence
You may fashion inference."
Still he paced up and down; his voice was low;
He glanced sidelong, but would not look at her:
"Here are two statements from my head,
Plucked and stated as they occur:
Philosophers are men," he said,
"And I am a philosopher.
What do you infer from these?"

"You are a man," said Heloise.

"Exactly, and you might have guessed,"
Said he, "but logically dressed
How inescapably conclusions rise!
Listen again."
                    He looked now at her eyes:
"All men have similar passions; men
Are also philosophers — what then?"

Heloise put her head upon one side,
And said: "Philosophers have similar passions.
Yet, must the middle be distributed?
Not all men are philosophers."

                              He frowned
And answered: "Let that be. I choose examples
Random. And now look closely, Heloise;
Sorites carries premises in three's:
    Men's passions all are similar,
    Philosophers are men,
    And I am a philosopher."
He gazed at her: "What then?"

Heloise laughed aloud, her white throat shaking:
"What then? that you, being philosopher,
Must check and guide the passions all men have."

Abelard turned away upon his heel:
"Logic, not ethic, is our demonstration.
You listen not to premises of reason,
But toss me maxims from a book of saws."

Unflickering bolts of sunlight cut his eyes,
And night's blue solace, softly burning stars,
A lost and withered surety. At last,
Pacing the broad planks of the floor's deep grain,
He turned and found her quiet eyes upon him,
Earth's guilt and glory folded in her lap
Between mysterious hands. He said:
                              "I thought
You would more easily know what I mean."
"I thought that I had answered what you mean,"
Said Heloise.
            He turned away again:

33

"You cannot know my meaning. You are young,
You are a woman. How can you know me?
You laugh at my hard words and syllogisms
Thinking that I design a simple thing.
You think you read my voice and guess at answers
Darkly knit into strands of self unknown
To me. How can you know?"

                    And Heloise:
"If knowledge is a name, can I not learn
Or guess it?"

             From her eyes the mockery
Suddenly fell: "If knowledge is a name,
I answered falsely. Women hear not words
But voices. I am insolent. Forgive me,
But logic, I thought, wore a long chaste robe,
And I am shattered finding her here dancing
Loosehaired and barefoot."

                Abelard flung out
His hands: "Will you unearth by vanity,
Woman's selfcredence, what is dark, I say,
Dark, difficult to me, philosopher
And fool? Very well. Take all. I confess
I teach tinsel. Logic is trivial
As harlotry, and knowledge that is knowledge
Is neither learned nor told."

                Heloise rose
And seriously faced him with her eyes:
"Then why have I a tutor?"

                  "Ask your uncle,"
Said Abelard, and paced away again.

"I ask you," she said calmly, "for it was you
Devised the plan. Vanity tells me that."

She stood motionless in the sunlit room,
White, like an arrow tipped and flying at him.
Thin lipped he stared and wondered, while she said:

"Last night why could we not begin our lessons?
Was it your daylight dialectic fancies
That mightily, after many tortured days,
Contrived you a decision? Yet by night
The ghost of a dead woman sphered all purpose
Into a crystal globe of abstinence.
And all through sleep my dreams and doubts were one,
For knowledge is a question in the night."

Abelard drew his breath. Volcanic trembling
Rose from his knees through ribs and shoulder bone
And made his lips mar words: "Oh, Heloise,
How should angelic fire, brushed from fleet wings,
Lodge in a mouth of mud? You do not know me.
My blood runs bitter in me, swept along
From roots of wormwood forests. My love twists
My hands behind me. If I stretch one out,
See how it shakes from the long agony!"

He held his hand to her. And Heloise
Drooped quietly her shoulders and her eyes;
She whispered: "Wormwood, then; my only flower."

He closed her in his arms, and she lay still,
Bound on his shoulder like a white scarf, gazing
Up at him with her quiet eyes, waiting
Implacable and helpless. He said nothing,
But holding her with arms that could have killed,
He let his kisses smite and sting her face,
And felt her answer stinging back. Then gently
Touching her foamless waterfall of hair,
He felt her shoulder quiver, and tears moisten
His neck. He raised her chin, but Heloise
Clinging and hiding in his shoulder whispered:

"Have you held up to me immortal mirrors?
Have you compared me, as you must compare me,
With the distilled white excellence of God?
All you have been may turn a rootless tree,
A ladder without rungs. I am afraid.
My love is Judas."
              "Yes," said Abelard;
"You have erased the names devised by Adam,
All language and all folly. Now my eyes
Are different. What I know is rounded, real
As God's first word. We speak and share His voice.
Our pool of light is small, but here we stand,
And flower is your name, because all flesh
Is petal to one everlasting rose,
Prismatic as the rainbow here to us,
White in His garden. Late philosophy
Comes trudging slowly after Heloise,
Bridging your intervals, and I perceive.

Who can know more? Who penetrates the night?
Who reads the flashed inscription of the stars?
Wonderful rings the iron in our earth,
Wonderful. Here is wet grass and misted tree,
With grasshoppers like brooches blade to blade.
Nothing is fearful here save not to know;
And I must know, whatever fears come smoking
Across our eyes. For there is clarity
Nowhere except in this white arc, your arms."

But Heloise sighed, murmuring: "Something dark
Stands waiting specterlike behind my hair,
Something alone and dark. You are a great man,
And so I must be wrong. And yet, you love me,
And so I must be right."
                Abelard laughed
And swept his hand all round her head, saying:
"That does not follow, but I am content.
Weave you the figures of this unknown dance
Whose passionate heel beats thunder on the stones.
Taut breath and muscle, wringing of moist hands
And longing eyes are all I know of it.
No, I know more. Mountains because of it
Become the glacier fluted colonnades
Of mind, and rivers talk a human tongue.
Our voice, our self, comes trumpeting back to us
Down canyons of the years that made us so,
And when those immortal feet stamp in the plain,
The gold wheat rises and unbinds its hair,
Leaves redden and descend, and hurricane winds

Scrub the earth clean for wearing white again.
This is your gracious dance. You have a task
To teach me more. Though once I lived far off,
Now I am living here and seeing you."

That night Arcturus, rising thin
And pure on Paris, gazing down
Saw the gargoyle's mocking grin
Unchanged above the silent town.
And the star, weary of the sight
Of gargoyles weariless of ill,
Asked in the language of the night:
"Gargoyle, are you gloating still?"

"Star," said the gargoyle, "I sit here,
You graze the walls of alabaster;
I too distill my knowledge clear,
So take my message to your master.
Say to him how it is time he dropped
The weeping and wailing and wages of sin;
The clocks of earth are never stopped,
The crops of life are never in."

"Laugh and be faithless," sighed the star:
"But what is born in the world tonight?"
"I am," the gargoyle said; "we are
The same in the world by any light;
And all goes well for one who sees.
The fun is here, if you must know:
Abelard lies with Heloise,
And weaves the purple through the snow."

IV

Arcturus turned his eye away
And diving softly down the sky
Bequeathed his kingdom to the day;
But rising earlier eve by eve,
He watched the springs of summer dry,
While the dogstar and the sun
Met and made their causes one,
With dust on kirtle, burr on sleeve,
With smell of powdery road, and musk
Of hedgerows scorched from dawn to dusk;
By day the waveless river flaring,
By night the gardens faint and still
With heavy wanton flowers, baring
To panting sky and cloudheaped hill
Impenitent blossom, kingly hues
Enraged by sun, revived by dews
Frail as resisting chastity;
Till milkmaids dropped their yokes and sat,
And seamen dreamed themselves at sea,
And churchmen knelt in the cool church;
And King Louis, surnamed the Fat,
Melting in silks, forsook his halls,
And seeking glades of pine and birch,
With country feast and slack estate,

Cooled his drooping majesty
By sibilant streaks of waterfalls.

But in the schools, the hot debate
Blew hotter, and the high pursuit
Of relative and absolute,
Of id and quid and hoc and quod,
And theorems piled high as God,
Raged on and on, though cheeks were wan
And eyes were gaunt, and sweat ran down
Inside each academic gown.
Till, like a skinless snake, Antoine
Crept to the vintner's shop, and falling
Upon a bench, sat there drinking
All quivering afternoon, until he heard
No more his universals calling,
Nor dreamed of entity or name,
Until two pupils of old Anselm came
And shouted, "Here is Abelard's pet bird
Pretending to be thinking!"

The other cried: "No, this is not his bird,
This is his footprint, left here long ago
Before he went away to Paradise.
His bird is slumbering in the gates of dreams
Sleeking her plumage for tonight."
                                        Antoine
Sat gloomily not answering, and watched
A cripple crawling toward him through the dust.
The others rang their glasses, and one cried:

"Abelard's rind is dry. The shoeless vermin
That listen in the gallery yesterday
Hooted like poultry at his contradictions."

He cackled in his beaker, and the other:
"Knowledge is nominal and real at once,
Rinaldus, doctrine hard for you and me.
But logic is not all. Oh, revelation,
When veils are split, and bodices are burst!
Tomorrow she will lecture in his place.
Well, he must sleep sometimes."
                                        The cripple inched
Aching through the sun. The other shouted:
"Now we can understand his praise of Sunday's
Twice needed rest!" And to the tune he sang:

*"How many and how bright are those
Dear Sabbaths when we never rose
        To query and be queried!
Ah then we played a sweeter harp,
And if my argument grew sharp,
        Lo, it was quickly buried!"*

Antoine was silent to the parody,
But heard still more solemnly mouthed behind him:
"Rinaldus, I am thinking of this glass.
The idea is a name of three solid
Dimensions with its buttocks in my brain.
Deny that, and I'll crack your quiddity
With the butt end of intellectus agens."

He tossed a drop of wine lees at Antoine,
Who watched the beggar and said nothing.
                                                        "No,
He only said, What I conceive is real,
And what you think is relative alone
To your dimensions."
                              "Ah, Rinaldus, there
We fail! Dimensions fail us. Socrates
Was wise because he learned Diotima's
Dimensions, and by night. He could spare sleep
With ease. But gypsy Abelard must sleep
Or be a red ant spitted on a thorn."

Below his eyes, the heap of twisted limbs
Held up to Antoine a palm cracked and colored
Like an old potsherd, murmuring of Mary
And saints and mercy. Antoine found a coin,
And through the dust the shipwreck crawled away
Toward the two others.
                              "Pay the spider, lad,
Or he will curse you. Abelard still teaches
Charity, and why not? He rolls in grace."
And Antoine shut his eyes. But one shrieked, "Bump
The rhythm, I will sing you my new song:

The lion of philosophy is learning to philander;
He teaches Heloissa what the learned books bequeath him.
By days she learns so much that he can scarcely
                              understand her,
But every night she's utterly beneath him."

42

Strangling his goblet Antoine stood and poured out
The gold wine in the dust. He slouched away
Dragging their laughter like a train behind him,
Till raveling thinly it was lost in duller
Sounds of the steaming city. Wandering
Alone, he climbed to Mt. Ste. Geneviève,
    And from his window watched the sun's
Red tyranny in sulphurous beakers boil
    Down, and ravening mist corrode
The burnished sky with blots of dark, like bronze
    Decaying; till across the roil
    Of scarring day, the cool stars showed
    Measure and mercy out of gloom.
    Then night by night, as at a loom
    Murmuring women tend the toil
Of shuttle and batten, from glimmering skeins
Quick threads flying, slow weights swinging,
    The stars worked, bathing blistered scald
    With poultice light; enticing rains,
    Mutely rebuking the sun's rage,
    And summoning winds, they sang and called
    To harvest, and blue spinster bloom
    Of asters; till their rhythm, singing
    Restrain, fulfill, aspire, assuage,
    Had stanched the summer's proud excess,
    And launched redeeming days, bringing
    Apple to barrel, grape to press,
    And wrangle of color to swamp and wood;
Days of prophetic pause, past equinox,
    When serfs all sing, and landlords reckon

4 3

By bushel and cart the season's good;
When listless mule and shambling ox
Doze and hear their steadings beckon,
And the last harvesters bend to truss
The ricks in rows of fading gold,
And barns rock with the fields' laborious
Desire heaped full and manifold.

And in his quiet cell, with flotsam shreds
Of Paris gossip washing at his walls,
Thibault reflected upon Abelard,
On faith, on reason, and on woman's love.
He rose, put on his hat with grave decision,
And firmly strode along the river bank,
Where Abelard, robed in voluminous
Reflections, footing druggets of dead leaves,
Had almost passed him by.
                              "Stop," cried Thibault,
"You man of exegesis, doctrine, dogma,
Deliberation and excursus, stop,
And speak to a poor brother of the faith.
You look ill."
                "I am well," said Abelard.

Beside the shining river, arm in arm,
They paced, Abelard silent. But Thibault:
"Besides the fact you live at Fulbert's house
With Heloise for pupil, or whatever,
Men seem to gather from your arguments
Your mind has failed. Oh, vanity's fine webs!

44

Men used to boast they could not understand you,
And obfuscation then was half your pride.
So cheap a noon now drizzles down to dusk:
Men grasp you suddenly; their boasts are changed,
Their pride is now, they have you in a trap."

"A philosophic trap, my dear Thibault,
Is quickly sprung, or if it catches you,
What difference does it make?"
                              "Fame," said Thibault;
"But more than fame, truth makes a
                              cogent difference."
Abelard laughed: "Truth is a mighty thing,
But only to the few who find it out."

"All," said Thibault, "in the end find it out.
God holds the end to which all flesh must come.
If you had faith instead of logic — "
                              "Faith,"
Said Abelard, "and logic are two eyes
Bored in the same poor brain that jilts itself
Deducing known from known in a half world.
I learn and map the other hemisphere
In loneliness, and build it as I go.
I watch the steel pommel of agony
Gleam from the belt of action. Danger lurks
In lifting of a finger. Do not smile.
I am not speaking of a thing you know;
You are enclosed, your cubicle complete,
As mine once was. In this new hemisphere,

45

A thin finger of fire precedes me, writing
The word compassion on vague human sand.
And there is nothing to enclose me here
But my own shadow, or the fire itself."

Thibault looked grave: "I used to laugh, believing
Your trivialities would come to peace.
The altar, the cathedra wait for you.
Where are you going now? This Heloise,
Where is she leading you?"
                                    "I tried to say,"
Said Abelard; "you did not seem to hear."

They paused and faced each other. The
                              bright stream
Crept on past children shouting in the shade.
Thibault murmured: "In time you will, you must
Recover; why not, I beseech you, promptly
Mend yourself? Early recognize a sin,
Early repent. Your prayer will let in grace,
And grace will heal your sickness."
                                    "Is it sin?"
Said Abelard. "I love a woman, build
New cloisters to my spirit's monastery
By letting between eye and written word
Her face drift, like a turning page; by hearing
In wind the slumber of her voice, by seeing
Aloft in the fixed mystery of stars
The glowing of her arm's white paradox.
Is this a sin?"

Thibault said icily:
"If it is fornication it is sin.
Loves differ; I divine you do not love
Heloise in the same breath with Aristotle.
I am not shocked. I only beg you think,
Madness champing its teeth at your good brains
Is making you a laughter in the schools,
And I commend you to true penitence."

"Penitence!" Abelard tossed in anger, "Penitence!"
Repenting is the easiest thing men do,
To cry peccavi, and creep back again
Into the safe and humble cubicle
For the free gift of grace. What of the laurel
That makes it shining to fly into thunder?
If this is sin, I take to me this sin,
For it turns grace to a brown stubble field,
And who in his right senses chooses stubble
Before the shadow of the green bay tree?
God's mercy, if it hangs by contrite hearts,
Will wait long to forgive me for this joy.
No, He may keep it. Let His thunder sing,
And I will sing replying, while I burn
In white fire, bathed in richer wrath than His."

Thibault looked at him, pale: "Your blasphemy
Spits on the Cross, curses the Holy Ghost.
Now you cannot repent. Your soul is damned."

"Words," answered Abelard. "You clutter me
With scraps and rinds of old patrologies.

47

I know their mumblings. But who knows of grace?
I only try my compasses: if they
Sweep true to circle, alleluia; if
They miss, I praise perdition that rings true."

"Christ's revelation fails in you," Thibault
Said fiercely; "heretic and apostate, merging
God in yourself, never yourself in God.
But He will burst you into fragments."
                                        "No,"
Said Abelard; "He keeps me whole. Bless you
For thinking God is always the same size.
He keeps changing; nobody really knows
How well He bears responsibility.
I look for more in me."
                        Thibault stood back;
His face was calm, but flickered, as a leaf
Spins flat in windless air. "My care for you
Turns ash," he said. "Scatter my words, my folly
Of altars and cathedras waiting for you.
Even returning late to the true faith,
Your only sacrament is penitence — "

"That word again," said Abelard.
                                "Farewell,"
Thibault said; "I abandon you to Satan."

He strode away, his dark robe like a sail.
Abelard took down reason from its shelf,
Unrolled it, and walked on by the bright river,

Quietly reading it; anger may rave,
But sometimes raves to the same tune as reason.
Full in his path ahead lay Notre Dame,
Whose spires trapped in the sun seemed
                              slender mist,
Quivering transparently, while as if hand
In hand Abelard and the sunlit water
Paced evenly together, hand in hand.
He muttered: "Fornication, penitence!
The point rests, but the line proceeds with music.
Thus from our infancy we age a little,
More than our autumns and our springs age us,
And in one day may live a thousand years
To know ourselves for more than perishable
Flung pebbles of creation."
                              All around,
As by the splitting of a sudden veil,
Light as it swept the air rippled with gold.
The world stood shimmering and flashed upon him
The instancy that lies in living things,
The inward shapes of water and of grass,
Of heavy trees and gnarled reflected roofs
That lay fallen in the river like dead leaves
Caught in the golden silt, and with it moving
Rippled forever toward the English sea.
Then it all faded, the earth closed her gates;
Abelard by the deep river wandered home.

V

"By moon and mirror," whispered Heloise,
"I am becoming mother Heloise."

Abelard took her quiet hands and said:
"This was decided long before it came.
While we are time's, let willingness trump will
And try a wonder beyond foresight. Come,
Bring us to birth! Now flowers merge, and milky
Warm flowing juices of your galaxy
Nourish the constellations. Here am I
Ready to be born upon whatever nine
The clock of your ecliptic voices bronze.
Fear's lamp is out of season on your face.
Frighten some other fool philosopher,
Not me. I am conceived. I shall be born."

But Heloise laughed weeping: "Lordly fool,
The harvest of this year of kisses comes,
Not you or I, but someone new. And now
My uncle will be angry."
                                    Abelard
Luxuriously laughed at angry uncles:
"He is enslaved. How reasoningly he coiled

Himself to pander you, visored in vice,
Engrossed in his own grossness. He bestows
His name upon my deeds, and magnifies
Himself by housing Abelard. Now let him
Roar or be still! We burst from rational
To real. By one obstreperous bulge of birth,
Inevitable as in a turned lock
The tumblers dropping softly into place,
Our silent blocks of mute hypothesis
Leap suddenly to form! Now can our words
Be wood or wheat field? Can our tokened touches
Become a boy, as a twig stuck in water
Bends to a new shape? Nature's every self
Yields other, while the wheeling mind,
                                   through spokes
Of spinning fire, peers for the hub of norm.
But every known turns strange, each birth
                                   of knowledge
Launches refractions in familiar waters,
Melts the moon, multiplies the stars, and tosses
Our mathematics to the worms."
                                   He smiled
Absently. Heloise said, "Peter, see?
My silver belt will not contain me long.
He is our death, if he finds out my belly."

Abelard laughed again: "Fulbert our death?
Death must have cause. Fulbert is an effect,
A mere result, rule bound to be the zero
His premises denounce him to."

She whispered:
"Death lurches from the smiling cedar grove."

He gazed at her and murmured: "Heloise,
I am here and alive, and hold your hands."

Her wet eyes opened wide: "Then let me go.
Hideous dreams defile me here. Let go,
And let me go."
                Then gravely Abelard
Released her hands, sat down and said to her:
"In Brittany an old gray castle stands,
Disclaimed once with my primogeniture
And dowered to Denise my sister. There
In peace she and the good seigneur Gerard
Farm our ancestral furrows; tottering calves
Each year are born, the orchards glow, the elm
Sprays upward from brown brooding loam;
                                white brooks,
Grey waxwings flutter in the smell of life.
Nothing is fearful there but dolmen stones
Windworn for centuries when Caesar came.
It is all there, and I will take you there."

"Buy me a horse," she said; "I will go there.
I hear you smiling at me, but I know.
You must not leave Paris."
                        "Leave Paris?"
Said Fulbert suddenly come through the curtains.
He sat and spread his hands upon his knees

As the room shrank too small and hot for three.
Heloise slipped to the bright window seat.
"Now who is leaving Paris?"
                              Abelard
Looked up and placidly said, "I."
                              Fulbert
Glanced wrinkling at him: "I divine your fear.
You feel sharp eyes, lewd faces. Grimaces
And murmurs, whispers. But you will come back?"

Abelard suddenly arose and laughed:
"Murmurs, no more? Emperor, Rome is ablaze
With slavering gutter fires! What songs they sing!
Listen:

> The Organon, the Organon
> Was Aristotle's tool;
> Abelard plies an organ
> Of the hedonistic school . . .

You see what you have done to me, Fulbert,
Tempting me here? I was a treatise once,
And now I am a ditty of Rudel.
The virgin muses of Mt. Ste. Geneviève
Lament me home, lost father, to the sober
Progeny of wisdom's wedlock, and the halls
Where midwife master I, like Socrates,
Tend intellects in crisis. Yes, and my own,
Alas, in harrowing labor cries to bear
In peace. But I live here, warming your fancy,
Teaching a girl conceptualism, a jest
Of streets, martyr of mud hilarity."

5 3

Fulbert stared dumb; Heloise motionless,
White faced, clung to the window seat. The
                                    spring sun
Dazzling the panes of diamond slid fingering,
Plucking her silken sleeve. Then Fulbert's voice:
"The day has struck. Flee promptly. Heloise,
The Master has a journey in his head.
Gather his books and gowns, for he must go."

Heloise went in silence. Fulbert leaped
Upright, and with his hand lifting to strike
Lunged forward. Abelard drew back and said:
"Spare me the vulgar bays of violence.
Our first estate asks reason . . ."
                                    Fulbert shouted
Quivering and red: "Violence or reason is it,
When the ewe, scarless, pastured to
                                    chaste meadows,
Lies mangled and the shepherd laughs? You, I,
Brothers in God, between whom pact and pledge
Should luster white as Holy Mother's hand —
Fire and filth you are, loose wind; quicksand
Of sophistry, solving trust into crime,
And truth herself into a troubadour!
Well may your barnful of longfaced disciples
Mourn for you martyred here, St. Venus' fool!
Vengeance can find you, Abelard. I am not
The impotence you image. Go now, go.
Your foot tracks in the dust of Paris streets
Are goatshape; statues in your memory

Are gargoyles, and all mothers in the realm
Will drag their daughters indoors when you pass.
Keep far from Paris. Once, recall, the doors
Clanged in your heresy's face, when long ago
De Champeaux read your blotted book clear-eyed.
Go, fling your eloquence on empty forest
And fatal sea. But never dare come back."

And Abelard to the red eyes of rage:
"Impotent and old you are. Did you trust me?
You thought it hard to dwell in a hot desert
Watching mirages of green water glide
And green palms waving by the waterbanks,
Green shadow and green comfort. That is hard,
Needing for restraint God's white and aging eye.
Your eye still flares a crater of red lust
Bored in the gray cocoon that nursed a down
Of wings in me for flight; now dry, punctured,
You envy, like De Champeaux. His door clanged
On challenge, not on heresy — yet look,
I drove my triumphing chariot home to Paris,
Charmed his blank listeners away, and next year
Shattered almighty Anselm at Laon.
Who sits now in De Champeaux's chair? Who pulls
The king himself by the ear, to perch schoolboy
To universals and theology?
Paris is mine. Sometimes she sings lewd songs,
Pretends fear, winces from me; but next morning,
Abelard, clovenfooted goat, behold
Panpiping by the rushes of the Seine

Hard doctrine, and our winsome city's heart
Is melodied. She sits with loosened hair
And girdle trailing in the ripple edge,
Unsandaled, simple, listening. She is mine,
Sunflower of my seedwork, faithfully
Uplifting eyes upon me, hour by hour,
As rainbowlike my arc ascends. Who knows
The end, Fulbert? Time's capstone is too heavy
For you or other mortal hand to lift
And mortar true. The end is process, endless.
Change is the end. Unending loops of change."

Abelard ceased. The sun at equinox
Blazing the diamond panes had moved
                              their shadows
Eastward an inch like dials on the sill.
Then in a hate-flawed voice Fulbert answered:
"Your wheels are falling, Phaethon; I shall lick
Rich vengeance up, better than blood on stones,
Watching your panorama of decay:
The world's wonder of disquisition makers
Lecturing to barren halls, a heretic
To silence damned, while teeth of retrospect
Sink leisurely and bitterly to bone;
Butt of the street boys at the last, hunted
Legend of glory, vanity and fall,
From town to town, frockless philosopher
Jeered away hungry; the brass vengeful feet
Following, curse and laughter following,
My laughter and my curse stamping your heels.

And Heloise will curse too from her grave,
Her coffined limbs' repentance hating you,
Face, voice and touch, her murderer — "
                                        Fulbert
Stopped suddenly; and Abelard: "Your dreams
Dance juggernaut. Heloise is not dead.
Your cursings bury her alive."
                            But slowly
Fulbert replied: "Her death to come, redeeming
The pulse of sin to silence, that grimed blood's
Memory vanish into holy song.
Yes, she will die. She will not think of you,
Nor recollect one feature."
                        Abelard
Threw up his head, laughed angrily and strode
Close to Fulbert: "Ah, she will recollect!
Woman's womb is a living diary
Of features. If the child resembles me,
Can you make her forget?"
                        Fulbert one instant
Stared, his face flat and void, then heavily
Dropped in a chair, his fingers at his cheeks;
And Abelard: "Our church is built on grass;
The spire drinks heaven, but the crypts chew dust.
To measure both in time, we meanwhile wear
Compassion's rose and lilies of restraint,
Frail mortal heraldry; come, reason upright:
My quest, through numbered grains of wrath
                                        and curse
All blowing where they must, pursues the haunt

And silver pace of God's free unicorn.
I leave you the red mutilation of rage,
Or glimmering daybreaks of benignity."

He turned to go. But Fulbert through his teeth:
"God's armament of fire upon your head!
You shall not ever see her face again."

He drove his pointing finger through the air.
Abelard, bowing slightly, like a man
Who hears a clock chime verdict, stepped across
The threshold. As he pulled the door, wide eyed
In the dim hall, Heloise caught his sleeve.
He took her hand and led her, neither haste
Nor hesitancy, to sunny streets, to horse
And westward out of Paris. And the sun
Diving before them down the afternoon
Glamored the dust with glory, while a screen
Clouding behind their kicking fetlocks grayly
Veiled and blotted the diminishing
Of Notre Dame and Mt. Ste. Geneviève.
They drove the night ahead, and shook away
Pursuit behind like moths out of a coat,
Till dawn and distance, caroling safety, slacked
Rein by an old village inn; there pausing
An hour, took one fresh mount for two asweat,
And Abelard held Heloise asleep,
Safe in his arms across his saddle bow
Her secret, and rode on toward Brittany,
All day and all the next, through windowed green

Of early woods, by jumbled streams, by farms'
Brown villeins laboring fenced; till
                            childhood lifted
Its face from the blue lake of distance, calling
Breton syllables to his drumming ears,
And smiling from known slopes haunted him home
To the red rooftops of his sister's barns
And steadings, and the antique knightly hall's
Mud court, grey wall, and crenelated keep.

Then stumbling serf and stately seneschal
Came out, hailing with shouts and bows
                            the pausing
Rider, and the seigneur Gerard strode forth
To greet the famed philosopher like one
Whose lands grow many; and Denise ran, wimple
Heedless, weeping her joy; but stood midcry
Hushed, and stared at her brother and the pale
Bluemantled Heloise who slept like death.

"Peter," she said, "Peter, why are you here,
And who is she asleep?"
                            And Abelard
Looked from his sister back to Heloise
In silence, sitting rooted, impotent
To lift her down or speak. At last his lips
Moved gravely: "She is mine, by God's great hand."

Denise said softly: "She is beautiful;
We had thought bishoprics of you, and yet —

Is she with child? Oh, Peter, if she lives,
What is to happen to her, and to you?"

He answered wearily: "I have returned
To learn the husbandry of wedded pastures,
To study churns and buttermilk and cheese;
To write a new theology. I left
The mothering dugs of earth out of the old.
Her name is Heloise. My arms and lips
Are numb. But I will answer everything."

Gerard reached up and lifted Heloise
Away, and Abelard got stiffly down
On the dark ground of his engendering.

VI

Castled in arrased cool of chambered stone
They waited. Spring conceived, labored and bore
A summer's brink of green days stumbling over
Sunblind, falling in pools of wakeless sky,
Hourless uncounted grass of time. Reclined
As in the arms of space, Heloise daily
Watched Abelard dispute the suns to dusk
And ribbons of red cloud, raising his quill
From time to time to tease her smiling cheek,
And tempt the autumn with its burden come.
And summer ceased her stumbling, buskined up
Her feet, and drawing down her lungs a matron
Breath, paced pondering her ceremony.

At a long orchard's end the dolmen stood,
A black stone terminus; beyond was moor.
The summer's inch of heat had not sunk far
In that dark ancient grain, and now the stone
Was colder than the firstling autumn wind.
"Why is it here?" asked Heloise standing
Under an apple tree. "Is it a tomb?"
Abelard slid his hand across the stone:
"The peasants say it was put here by Merlin,
And some say giants. But there once were men

Who raised these rocks; no, not for tombs, for temples
Oriented by stars for sacrifice.
Now it divides the orchard from the wild,
And rain has washed away its frightfulness."

Heloise touched it: "Temple? Is it ours?
From Notre Dame to twilit dolmen stones?
My window looks toward apples ruddying
The orchard, but across the distance always
Stares back this stony watcher of the trees."

Abelard laughed: "Beseech the apple tree
For teachings of the ripe hour. Come midwinter,
We shall be parents. Fear, like this tawdry net,
Torments your hair's true gold. Unknot this nonsense,
And see, you are a woman full of child
Safe here in Brittany with me."
                                        He pulled
And threw the clasps away, and shook her gently.
And Heloise, her hair about her face:
"Here safe; here yours; hereafter what will come?"

And Abelard: "Am I an idle man?
If underfoot the faulted rock should slide
And earthquake shunt me elsewhere, I will stand
Elsewhere. And here I stand. Here I devise
Our dignity, and you shall marry me
When we return to Paris."
                                        He paused, smiling
Gently, then laughing aloud: "How a man

Shifts houses! From the knighthood of these hills
To the white hill philosophy, from there
To Fulbert's house; now in a cavernous dolmen
Building a burgherhood!"
                        He strolled two paces
Into the dolmen's shadowy heart, and glancing
Back at her standing at the sunlit gates,
He saw her faintly smiling as she said:
"Below your lectern shall I crouch pinning
Blankets to a baby, folding swaddling clothes
While scholars hoot? O Abelard, logician
Who plots his love's impetuous act on square
Coordinates of theorem himself!
What will you prove by marrying in gown?
You did not make me up; you cannot prove
Me, Heloise, loving and ruinous.
I am your mistress, let me die of it."

Hearing her laughter, Abelard frowned and said:
"Must I be hooted at by infidels
For taking sacrament? As if wedlock cried
Forfeit of intellect and argument,
And all that makes the philosophic day's
Long dewlapped fraud! I am not priest nor monk,
Though many a bishop, churchly beast of prayer,
Keeps private feasts to feed his public famine.
To save myself from that, and as God's plough
First furrowed soul in flesh, let me invent
A priesthood of the mind's lamp trimmed by love.
The aging scholar of Mt. Ste. Geneviève,

6 3

Choking with his own dust, is marching forth
In wedding clothes, and listen, birds and bells
Of morning hymn the wayward novelty."

Long silent, Heloise stood turned away,
Her loose hair blowing in the harvest wind,
Her face a marble mask half quick with sun,
Half shadowed by the dolmen's jaw. At last
She said: "I am beginning to learn shame.
Our deeds till now, our daylight sins, defiance
Of the sun's piety and mouths that howled
Contrition and confession — oh, not I,
I have not been ashamed! Do not make me
Ashamed! Must we do more? I have no more
To give or do. Your mastering gaiety
Builds high, but my heart prophesies of skulls.
This dark arch peering at me through the apples
Tempts and terrifies me. Oh, this was not
The gift I meant for you. I cannot give
My wish for the snuff of challenge in the wind
That drives you. Like a fear it drives you — "
                                        "What?"
Cried Abelard; "What fear?"
                              "Oh, not afraid,"
Said Heloise, "and yet, so deep in fear
That footed on safe earth at last, you prowl
And drag up screaming mandrakes from the soil.
Your hands are like a clock's inexorably
And stiffly signaling hours on and on,
Processions into dark no man can read.

64

Oh, Peter, yield to me! This antic vaunt,
You, canon of the high cathedral school,
Married in office! They will pull you down!
Think of my uncle, count your enemies;
Your doctrines jog with heresy; beware
Me worst: my arms around you crack your pillars,
My hair ends tangle with the shoes of death.
Listen to me, Peter, listen; you are chased
By challenges. Batten your ears and go
Safely to your own house, where never fall
Is fatal, never sin is Judgment Day.
Go, leave me while you still are Abelard."

Abelard twisted his mouth sourly:
"Am I still Abelard? Then I am bored
With being Abelard, and pray new torrents
Wash me to provinces of livelier conquest!"

Heloise, thrusting out her hands, cried, "What?
The conquest of fool's paradise, possession?
What do you fear?"
                    He laughed: "I have no fear."

But Heloise, half angrily: "Yes, fear
That gropes for fireside safety, knowing where
And when, till cake is dry and milk is curd.
Love cannot live in safety; love must haunt
A precipice, lame and blindfold."
                                  Abelard
Gazed at her gravely: "Yes, but what if love,

6 5

Knowing his enemy, drinks down the challenge
And taunting safety's peril, blind and lame
Dives into dungeons of unrisking peace?
Oh, try no falls of paradox with me,
You, who one instant threaten me with danger,
The next with safety. Is this argument?"

Heloise drooped her head, but Abelard
Stroking it said: "Unmesh your thoughts. Hear me:
From every turret of desire, since first
Falcon wish pointed wing, one challenge trumpets:
How much can any man preserve his own?
Who can escape that challenge? Is there shame
In such coercion?"

                "Shame?" cried Heloise
Flinging her head up with tear startled eyes;
"Not shame — the danger of your life!"

                             He said,
"The danger of my life is, I was born."

She stepped under the dark roof of the dolmen,
Beneath whose liturgy of glimmering stone
All sounds of the bright afternoon were hushed.
And gazing at the dim grass floor, and reaching
To find his hand, she said: "Give years enough
To ruins, and their edges melt, soft ivy,
Brave lichens grow. Could we not have such years?
Could we not live a little while?"

                         But he:
"If love can house a choice, I rightly chose.

66

We shall not lurk wide provinces apart.
We live to roof the gable of our choices,
And if death builds the cornice, let it shine."

She let her faint hand wander over his.
"My heart puckers," she whispered shivering.
The wind lamenting through the megalith
Cooed under the capstones.
                        "You are cold,"
Said Abelard; "come out into the sun."
He drew her by the hand, but suddenly
Her arms leapt up around him, and her fingers
Sank in his hair: "Abelard, Abelard,
Forget, kill, anything but marry me!
Or else forget the rest, and here, not battlemented
In that baronial pride of towers, but here
In this black dolmen's penitential cell
Dwell pasturing on dear immediate joy
Sheltered in shadow, till the shadow's mercy
Rhythms our walls, and bare stone looks benign."

Putting her hands off he laughed curtly: "Here
In Brittany? This dolmen? Ruins, ivy,
And brave lichen indeed, while sogging rains
Dig down our founding stones each year an inch!
Welcome our child here to bland Brittany's
Prefashioned order of processional trees.
I was born once in Brittany; this time
It must be Paris, where the shouting hours
Create me new and suckle me on time — "

But he paused, staring at her tears; she said:
"I know my venomed herbs; I know my late grass
Broods other spring, not yours. Peter, hear me!
Go back to Paris when our child is born."

Abelard gently smiled, then drawing her
Close, kissed, and calling to her eyes, answered:
"I say, not in ourselves, but where men hear
And change for hearing lie our galleries;
Not yet, love, in the dome of melted time
Whose midnight tolls once a great year, not yet.
Of Breton matrix, yet of you, still dawns
In Paris my nativity. I feel
It prance; I feel the light bulge, and the earth
In labor of my issuing shoot anguish
Quivering through many-hoofed humanity,
For years when Muses were our mothers, when
Immortal serpents in the violet hills
Coiled round a godly infant, pouring death
And vision into blood he might foreknow.
Since then, our centuries were slept away.
Now from their somnolent old scouring foam
Venus awakes, wish rankling into pearl
Rises to anthems of the wind, announcing
In rains of red and snowy roses, while
White spotless beasts attend and verdurous trees
Bend smiling tranced, announcing to the rocks
Whose old skin creeps and prickles, the sharp cry,
Our birth for learning and for listening, ours.
Banish the dirges from your eyes. You shall

Be mine, veil, ring and benediction. Mine."

Heloise drew away; her voice came trembling
And cool: "You flood me. I hear nothing, nothing.
I will not marry you."
                        Then Abelard
In abrupt fury gripping her arms drove
Her helpless to the dolmen's wall, her bare
Elbows upon the arctic touch of stone:

"Whose hands are these? Whose voice is
                        judgment? Whose
Fullness has made your breasts and belly big?
You shall be mine because you are mine now.
What is must be, and I will kick to rags
The dragons coiled in your brain's shuddering cave,
And marry you though seven anathemas
From seven triple hats should damn me for it."

She rolled her head against the rock, biting
Her lip; and he unlocked his hands, but she
Still leaned shaking against the stone, murmuring:
"Is this the end of consecration? Shame's
Nudity pilloried against noonday?
Love builds a temple, but in time its columns
Crumble, its blocks turn sodden, fatal stars
Fall through the ulcered rafters; in the end
A frozen monolith, that one gold hour,
Garlanded with denial, given and slain
At the white altar, might — but now the gift

Revokes its mystery."
                    But Abelard
Shook his head, answering with a voice and smile
Of twilight: "You, my golden hour, shall stand
At the white altar garlanded; the gift
Is still to give. Wait fearless. You shall see."

And Heloise said nothing. But the sun,
Searching the late west with a smoldering lamp,
Shot through the stone's night freighted corridor
Red silted rays which lit along the walls
Ridges and crevices, and made appear
Cuneiform aslant, illegible
Spiked messages of shadow, pointed where
The arch of night was rising in the east;
Where slowly they, with bridal fingers linked,
Followed their shadows through the orchard home.

VII

And through the shadows of theology
Toward promises of thunder, threats of smiles,
Through halo-burnished heads toward everlasting
The Burnisher, Abelard drove his pen
Days long in a high tower chamber, sitting
By light of a one shafted window slit,
One white ray on a page half written. Three
Candles stood by if day should die too soon.
And though he looked down on the tallest elm,
Sometimes he felt the greenery of boughs
Tinting his page with earthen ideographs,
Until he asked, How high can the trees grow?
But soon the trees with opening fingers fountained
Slowly downward foundering gold. He wrote:
"All seasons are one moment to the mind
Of instant making and retaining love."

In the far distance he could see the dolmen
Unchanged by season. Not an apple still
Bent branch, and first white freezing tokens stung
The fields aware of winter. Letters failed
From Paris. Advent, steering by the star
Of birth with black and purple sails hushing
Hilarity, sailed the hours toward Bethlehem.

In Brittany the pallid straw fires hissed
The lingering demons from the stubble lands.
And suddenly all bells at midnight rang,
And angels' glorias and puissant wings
Beating and crying the Nativity
Swept through wide winter space of blue and stars
With vigil alleluias. Abelard
Stood in the lectern of the minster, high
Above the congregation to pronounce
A sermon, the first Mass of Christmas ended,
And all were still to hear the famous tongue:

"This text, and God so loved the world, might be
Genesis, love's commandment of the mold
In instant making. God so loved the sea
He made it, kissed the sun into a flame
And moon a mirror, cutting passion out
Of stern deliberate dream, His building will.
And later, when the sons of God beheld
Daughters of men that they were beautiful,
Those goodly sons of God, obedient angels,
Foresaw through history a strict design
Of earth and heaven, like two mighty magnets,
Drawing each other slowly into union.
But heaven's love is never satisfied.
It stabs the earth with grace. God, caught in time
At last, turning from order glimpsed detail,
Centrifugal hands appealing from the core
To the periphery, the sheen and glance
Of surfaces, where soul in anguish veiled

Peers with the tension of a lute string. Then
It was that God so loved a woman, He
Abandoned sky and scope and axled orbits,
And came down full of splendor. Grace came down
Like golden rain, came down like mumbling cloud
Around recipient limbs, like a swan's feather,
Like a white bull he wooed, and like a lion
Went crowned again to heaven, and there waited.
Had He created her? Oh echoing jest!
Think of the tawny beast lounging aloft
Waiting time caught, while she created Him.
And she, fragility of flesh, trusted
To free omnipotent Futility
Himself. Bored with His being, bored with making,
He let her do it for Him, like a lover
Who dreams himself within his mistress' womb
For comfort first, and then for second birth.
And she so loved Him that she did it for Him,
Toiled with that ponderous divine pregnancy,
And turned the love of Heaven to a trifle.
For who indeed loved more, the Maker making
All to His taste, or she whose soul, peering
Anxiously into time's unknowable,
Eased Him of life unworthy of His creatures
And gave Him back, as He must now become?
For God so loved the world that He became it."

But at the church gate later the priest said:
"I am a sinner and have often failed
In charity. But I thank God at least

I never spoke such heathendom before
The high altar on Christmas eve."
                                    "The Bull,"
Said Abelard, "crosses his wings before
His face sometimes. All you can see is feathers.
Catch him in flight, the flogging hoofs, the horns
Low, harrowing hell. Peace to your piety,
Goodnight."
                    And he returned to Heloise,
His churchless bride who feared the flare and stare
Of candles on her girdle. By a fire
She waited for him, and she sighed and said:

"I see that you have given in this parish
Your last sermon. And yet I thought a savior
Might mollify your magnanimity.
Did you remember there to pray for me?"

Abelard touched her hair: "If it is prayer
To satanize and preen my intellect
With metaphors of magic named for you
And prank in inner sanctums, yes, I prayed.
How utterly unholy bark the throats
Of bells to unbelievers! Faith is dark
And secret as a starlit hour alone
Aloft a magian's astronomic tower
High built toward horror where the night folds close.
Rhomboids of constellations fashion fear
From beltless wilderness; and triangles
Of anguish print the self of sights and smells

Over the ductile spate, the spendthrift waste.
Then words are things, and well bred order reigns.
The bells bang it all out of my head. I hear
Tympana storming in the mountain glens,
And order is a glint of gold hair dashed
In cascades over swelling nipples, words
Are nowhere in the night of procreation.
Yes, my last sermon here or anywhere.
The tongue is terrible."
                                Heloise smiled:
"Nativity is always night. The chime
Of planets in the midnight sky announces
What turns untrue for telling. Look behind you
At your epiphany."
                        He turned and saw
Along her pointing hand the morning star
Tingling moistly afire in a black oblong
Of windowed sky. Abelard watched a while,
Then said:
                "And yet with eyes of dust I see,
Standing on stone, hard dust; the window's frame
Was built by the bloodthreaded dust of hands.
He needed dust for measuring. What of stars?
Do I need them, or just my dusty eyes?"

Heloise said: "Am I the dust in them?
I saw you once a solitary star."

He looked at her unhappily and sighed;
And suddenly he left her standing there,

And climbed up to his study, lit the three
Wax candles, and sat down, through promises
And thundering threats, through halo-
                    burnished bones
Of saints, to drive his pen toward everlasting
The Bone Burnisher. And Christmas
                    morning dawned.

Twelve days of feast dwindled away to mere
Midwinter. Restive with the climbing season,
Cursing the absence of his library,
Abelard worried sheaves of manuscript,
And wrote long letters to Mt. Ste. Geneviève
Asking for books, and no books ever came.

"Lost in the snow. No one can travel now,"
Gerard said calmly. "All those learned words
Soggy and sunk in drifts. I doubt they tried;
I doubt your luckless messenger arrived."

So trapped in the white mornings Abelard
Would rise and watch the serfs coughing
                    and stumbling
Among the barns, foddering animals.
Blue smoke arose to blue air windless, birdless
Save for gulls carving lofty circles over
Hills voiceless, trackless, and the humble fields.
Life lay indoors, while winter giants hurled
White spiteful splendor on the prostrate land.
Abelard shivered, sighed, wrote, waited, slept.

"Too late to go back now," said Heloise.

Winter was window high when dozing early
Heloise lay one evening, and woke suddenly
And knew someone was coming. Abelard
Called to Denise, and waited with Gerard
By a cold window. Blue and silver played
The blast of the deep winter quietly
Across the little hills of Brittany.
The dolmen wore the snow in winnowed veils
Streaked from its rocks, in soft windsilken alps.
Answerless ages of its mystery
Climbed skyward, as night turned, through
                              rifted boulders
Timing the hour lines of meridian stars.
Abelard stood by the window for two hours,
And turned at last into the room. He said:

"I thought that being came down in white squares
And triangles, first measurements of space,
Spinning on perfect axles, printing soul
On matter. Pity folly such as mine,
Who never before stood in the cold draught
Of midnight, wondering brown heads or gold,
By what dear countless chance come flesh and hair,
And hands to hammer courage. How can I
Have learned so much, and never learned the earth?"

"We never learn a thing too soon or late,"
Gerard said; "Everything is just on time."

Abelard paced. The shivering beast below
Waits, while she does it for him. Suddenly
He cried: "Who is to be born? Who dies? Who dies?"

Gerard said: "Birth has many a false start,
False labor, and false fear. The child will come.
This edge of France is like the edge of life;
Here with ourselves we live, our comings, goings,
Properties of ourselves; midwives and priests,
Earth-crumbling sextons, and ourselves besides."

And past the naked orchard far away
The snowcapped dolmen glittered in the moon.
From winter haunted valleys the wind soughed
And mingled with the muffled sound aloft
Of cries and creaking doors, and Denise singing
Hymns, and the stamp of servants heaving logs.
Oh, greet the newborn with a smiling fire,
While night measures and dawn begins to come;
For silence like the dropping of sea wind
Follows. Gerard was dozing. Abelard
From the top stair of daybreak brazen-eyed
Gazed back on valleys of his fear. His blood
Laughed, and he ran upstairs calling Denise,
And met her by the door.
                              "A son," he shouted.
She drew the blankets gently: "Yes, a son.
Heloise is asleep."
                    But Abelard
Had pushed the door.

Bare heavy breasts and arms
Flung bare on bolster hills, half risen from
The furrows of the bed, lay Heloise,
Her dawnlit hair like summits of the morning,
And her vein-swollen hands languid, leaning
Limp as from gripping the two poles in anguish
To bear plains, mountains, oceans. Abelard
Shrank as the hot wind of the chamber steamed
Across his face. Heloise had not heard,
And Denise closed the door. But Abelard
Stood staring down upon the stones, a sound
Like sistrums ranting in his head, a roar
Of lion wind. Then up the coiling stair
He went again, and found his study bright
With winter morning. The long manuscript
Lay flat and white. He took it tranquilly
And tore it end to end, across, across,
Struck tinder in the grate and lit the shreds,
Murmuring, "O mountain flame, O Phrygian fire!"

Haunted still by such echoes, Abelard
One morning gazed down gravely at his son
Who squinted in the clash of light on snow.
"His name," he said, "is Astralabe, for such
He is; a living armillary sphered
By circled reason, turning clockwise hours
Shapely and same; and difference, as he chooses,
Wandering opposite, speedy or slow,
Ploughing the troughs of quickness and decay.
Order and measure. Therefore Astralabe."

Heloise raised her eyes: "Is that a name?"
He murmured, "Things will not ally with names.
I have no thoughts except old foolishness."

Then as he looked at her, again the flame
Scorched reddening across his eyes, his temples
Echoed a mountain scored by cataracts;
Delved thunderbeaten brows recessed his gaze,
His smile began and broke, and he said: "Once
I loved a nunnery of doctrines; I,
Archbishop winter, mitred lordly white
And crosiered with the solstice of December,
Wimpled their placid foreheads and pure chins
With snowy wisdom's starch. Now what has come?
Hills change, my summits lose their sanctities,
And summer climbs above the timber line;
From frozen silence water trips and purls,
An ivied head, a thyrsus laden hand
Mounts a turf pulpit stung with fiery flowers.
Space shakes again her elements to chaos,
And miracles are done on reason's rapier,
Whose widthless line is squared into a plane,
And on the plane is built a pyramid.
How can I wield such weaponry? How lift
Words weighed with Egypt's kings, their
                              mummied heads
And magic hieroglyphs, their centuries
Of sandy death, their humanheaded birds
And basalt, lotus capitals of dreams,
Their royal life pulse holding bodily

Embalmed amid four watchful goddesses
Dead beauty like a geometric star?
I lose myself here, winning skills of death
And pride, the mind of a sarcophagus
Cradling its lovely wasting jewel. Courage
Is born of decay's kiss."

                    Heloise took
His hand; in crystal of the window glare,
Her arms and face of crystal, quietly
She said: "And is it courage to kiss death?"

And he: "I never dreamed the helpless power
Of this, my newest infancy. I challenge
Multitudes, knowing nothing, out of tongue
And pocket of all speech. Let Paris hear."

She said: "Let me beseech it all again.
Here is your son, and here am I, both yours;
The land is yours, this also is the world.
Here warm with us, where choice has led, remain."

Abelard smiled: "The wish of peace, wan, easy
Peace with betrayal. Paris waits for us."

Heloise cried: "Your Paris is a scream
Of terror in my sleep! I hear the boots
Of death scuffing its gutters. Go then, go,
Challenge, belabor, win. But go alone.
Marry a muse, not me. Leave Astralabe
And me to hoard our safety here for you."

Abelard rose and in a far voice said:
"But where I go, marriage or martyrdom,
Body or memory, indifferent choice,
I carry you, and scheme no other way."

Heloise gazing down, her head curving
Over the newborn as in lamentation,
Murmured, shrouding the blanket round young eyes
From the untender light: "Then let spring come
And take us, for this winter's work is done.
Bright bitter snow will furl itself away
In huddling streams. Sleep out a long farewell
To this wide sky. When spring comes, we shall be
Where doddering houses put their heads together
And plot shadows."
                    Abelard slowly turned
And said: "You need not fear for Astralabe.
We, being one, must go. He must await
His own comminglings of his deeds and self.
We two must go. But not with Astralabe."

She flashed her face up at him. Abelard
Locking his fingers, twisting them, said: "Patience,
Denise will nurse him well. When we return,
We then — "
                    But he broke off, seeing her eyes
Glazed like the cold fire of an agate. Awed
Mute as the fingers of that silent rage
Fastened on his stomach, he stared fixed; bondage
Of eyes blotted with hard glare, like midwinter

Sun on a cold sea, both stared blind, and neither
Turned as a hinge croaked, and the door swinging
To footfalls showed Denise and Gerard standing
In stately robes and fur, with golden chains,
Gem crusted sword and keys at girdle jingling,
Seigneur and chatelaine dispensing feast
And hightide for the hailing of an heir.

"What is it?" cried Denise. "Your faces look
Like snowbanks. Come, Peter, the seneschals
Roast ox, red bungs leap from the cask; come down.
Our people stamp for you and Astralabe.
Listen to the loud songs."
                              But Abelard
Said nothing. Heloise, her eyes still hard
With agony and hate, said: "You shall not
Carve us apart. You care for triumph, I
Care nothing. Are you dust and shadow, like
All flesh, or a dried peeling of the moon?
This is no foundling out of foreign space,
But body out of body. Go alone.
This is too soon a loss. I will not go."

Then Abelard quickly: "No, not soon; the snow
Is deep. Not until spring; we shall return
In time, a little time. Denise will nurse him
Well till we come."
                              Denise, sucking her breath,
Sat close to Heloise: "What do you mean,
Peter? Whom will I nurse?"

                              And Abelard:
"Only a little time. Lest we devour
Our making, we must trust our son to you,
A little time. Grim faring waits for us.
Heloise — "
                    But Heloise said: "Blood is fierce,
Peter. Beware, there is a curse in blood."

But her voice shook; she flung her head upon
Denise and wept. Then Gerard, fingering
His chain reflectively and smiling, said:

"Peter, these lands are yours, green and peaceful
Except when Anjou clinks unmannerly
Brass heels along our marches. A good life,
Much time for hunting or philosophy,
And no hard choice, I think, if I were you.
Here I would keep her, getting old and kingly
By the kind seasons. Breton soil creeps round
Your feet and holds you. You, who parted young
For the great world, you never knew your lands,
Your own hills, your own sea . . ."
                                        "But now I do,"
Said Abelard; "my son is born to them.
Childless yourselves, pass him the seigniory,
And do not tempt me from my loud shores inland.
I have not finished with Mt. Ste. Geneviève,
Friends, enemies, disputes, all noisy things,
All parcels of my luggage through the world.
I have not asked the parting kiss from life."

Gerard smiled dimly, but Denise leaping
Up, and with fervor grasping Abelard's hands,
Cried:
        "Must you? Why must you? Yielding right to me
You robbed yourself of safety. Here, behold
Yourself again bronze baron of these lands,
And Lady Heloise! I give back all.
Share walls and acres here, and keep your child."

Abelard touched her cheek murmuring, "Is it
So easy to be belted, landed, titled,
Secure in armories and walls? I have
No skill at baronies. The serfs would laugh.
I am a churchman."
                "Churchman," cried Denise
Scoffing. She wheeled away muttering, "Mad
Peter, you think you can do everything,
Reckless what happens."
                "Yes," said Abelard;
"Since all things done are done by someone, why
Not done by me? And as for happenings,
By hindsight or by foresight, I must answer
Happenings as they come, by such lame logic
As pounds me piecemeal or emblazons me."

Denise in silence let her hand wander
On Heloise's shoulder. Gerard blinking
Slowly stared at the floor. Then Abelard
Said sorrowfully: "Dangers born of me
Are mine, but Astralabe becomes himself.

Though once I fancied he and I were one,
In widening deltas, who can know what hills
Conceived us, or what trees our waters feed?"

He looked, but saw no sign from Heloise.
Abelard turned back from her hidden face
To the bright window of midwinter, watching
The snowy hills invisibly preparing
New seasons. And he bowed his head, nodding
To the white hills, nodding for spring to come.

VIII

And spring came with a letter in her hand:
"Master," it ran, "have you forgotten us?
The stones of scandal smash our study windows.
Rome hates your yeas and nays. Anathema
Stinks in the air like sulfur after lightning.
In Clairvaux Bernard steams with Vandal hate,
And brews a bishops' council at Soissons.
Come soon or not at all to those who wait."

"Who writes this epitaph?" asked Heloise.

"Antoine," he said, "my pupil; we must go.
Bernard, almighty priest political
Of Christendom, who tucks popes, cardinals, kings
Under his cassock, hates my yeas and nays!"
Abelard laughed and tore the letter up:
"Let it break hard and loud, and the wind blow
The crystal goblet from the altar cloth!
Bitter temptation to announce me whole
Now, an unreasoned shout, myself. Not yet;
I can be subtle though it stings. We must
Knit bonds at first in secret, while this duel
Racks the stump limbs of thought to crucial stature.
Be comforted. I am angry. I shall win."

She answered nothing. Abelard muttered fiercely:
"Win there, lose here! Nature herself confutes
The sanctities she argues me to find.
Who knows renunciation from betrayal?
Save that easy salvation is a sieve
That strains the flow, and cheats the springs of life."

He waited for her answer. She looked old
Suddenly as he watched her, sorrowing
And old, still as a stained-glass penitent.
"Heloise," he murmured. She smiled up to him,
And gave her hand: "The springs of life are dear,
Dearer than all precious waters, dear as you.
Take me to Paris. Let the water flow."

She met his eyes, and saw the severing
From Astralabe, the long fear-pitted road
To Paris. But they said no more that day,
Nor many a night of tattered sleep; until
A dawn came when two horses stamped the thawing
Clay in the courtyard, level sunlight sleek
On haunch, glinting at bit and studded reins.
Cool in their nostrils whitened the damp smell
Of night and earth. Air's early reticence
Still folded hill to hill in silted light
Of gold, where the road curved and rose and stretched
Away into the far silence, waiting.
Denise wept by the gate; but Gerard stood
With Heloise, who holding Astralabe
Tilted her head to watch his blue eyes gaze.

"He sees the sky," Gerard said. Heloise
Nodded hard. From the orchard pealed aloud
The joy of nesting birds. Heloise said:
"Yes, here I know, here in this wind not ours
He should breathe deep and grow. Before we come
Again, he will be up on two feet, prancing
Among the apple trunks. Sometimes, Denise,
Let him run naked with the trees in summer,
Let the sun have him. For the trees will die,
Also the sun will die . . ."
                              She hid the rest
In the warm swaddlings. From the hall adroitly
Stepped a groom with burdens for the journey.
He strapped them firmly to the horses' cruppers
And stood at beck. At last came Abelard.
He looked at them and smiled:
                              "My son is heir
Legitimate to all our lives. Remember.
Far more than trust, a lost theology
Beats in his blood. And there are days to come."

He came to Heloise, and touched her arm.
Lifting her head, she looked around the three,
Raised her eyes once to Abelard, then slowly
Walked to Denise, and stretching out her arms
Gave Astralabe, whose eyes blinked as the hands
Changed under him. And blindly she turned back
To Abelard, who lifted her and mounted.
The groom stood off with head atilt; then slow
Hoofs punched the soil, and carried them past gate

And bridge. And at the road, Heloise once
Flung her arm backward, but downhill the hoofs
Broke into cantering.

            And so once more
They came below the walls and weathered gates
Of early love, at duskfall in a rout
Of homing laborers, with staves and spring's
Mud clotted shoes, among tall hunchback houses
Hooding the stench of crippled streets. And there
They sheltered by the red hearth of an inn,
Where Antoine, waiting with embrace and wine,
Gaiety and long gossip, laughed them late
Asleep.

       But in the frail shimmer of dawn,
Abelard, rising like a hunter, snared
The bishop's self in bed; who, stormed by love
And eloquence, routed by a hundred proofs
And paradoxes treating sacraments,
Before the sun had touched his window, promised
To join and bless by night in secret chapel.

So one more day they housed in hiding. Then,
At midnight in the crypt of Notre Dame
The altar of the Blessed Sacrament
Was all aflame. The bishop paced alone
Across the stones, the sacerdotal prayer
Ash as a dry finger at his lips,
And in his conscience motes, and in his eyes
Thorns of fear. To a hurrying pulse of steps
He turned, and Abelard stood in the door

Holding a woman veiled. The bishop stepped
Between the chancel rails and said:
                              "By love
And reason, Abelard, and friendship too,
Consider, spare. Bernard of Clairvaux wields
Words that are bludgeons in the dark; for you
The walls and streets are haunted. Spare this woman
And spare me sin. The promise I have given
Poisons me."
              Abelard spoke lipped with fire:
"A gargoyle rides your tower, and his song
This rainy night garlands with sorcery
The house of sacrament. I know my danger.
I am unshriven, unconfessed. I knocked
A taunter down in the dark. But here I dwell
In Paris, and I marry what is mine,
Be it by the black mass with your most horny
Curse on my head. If you refuse, I find
Another. Yet, remember how you said,
Love issues its own sanctity. To say
That once and not to lie, you must reach out
Beyond the garden, beyond cushioned hills
Flattered with flowers, beyond hope of days,
And scratch upon your patient coffin lid
Your name."
              The bishop pressed his palms together.
"God cleanse us all," he murmured. "Join your hands."

They clasped and knelt to gentle whispering
Of syllables that flowed on patterned stones,

Mosaic on mosaic. Abelard
Stared at the seal ring on the bishop's hand,
Then at the one he would give Heloise,
And then at Heloise herself. But she
Was nowhere in the chapel; he was marrying
A veiled woman he had not seen before.
With terrible quick fear he swept the veil
Away, and found her face tear drenched and white.
He whispered, "Is it you?"

                      "Not I," she said.
"You marry times and things I never was."

The bishop paused. "Finish," said Abelard.

And out of incensed air the cross was carved,
And rain of benediction sprinkled softly
The damp and veilless hair of Heloise.

But in the morning Abelard struck his hands
Together, calling Antoine: "Go, Antoine,
To Mt. Ste. Geneviève, and on our door
Publish my coming. We have skulked enough.
I speak tomorrow at my hour."

                            Antoine
Answered: "To some your news is gray already.
A letter came this morning."

                            Abelard
Broke seal and read the writing: "Must you hide
In hostelries? My fire is hot for you.
Seek shelter. Friends are few. I wait. Fulbert."

Heloise reading by his shoulder shook
Her head: "His bridal gift is bloodshed. Tear
The paper, send the tatters back to him."

But Abelard: "Fear, fear! The old man's house,
If he has brewed these months to peace, could roof
Our torn gable with honor for a day.
And if he spits on peace, all Paris is
A spiked well. Antoine, go to Fulbert too,
Say we shall come."
           And when Antoine was gone,
With a long kiss he lulled her shaking flesh,
Calling her wife and bride, till gloaming rays
Reddened the window like a rising bruise,
And summoned them to keep their interview.

IX

Fulbert's great hearth flamed, and the raftered room
Was slashed and shot with the red silk of fire
Like a rich courtier's sleeve. He turned to greet
Their entering. "Dear prodigals," he said,
"Piety is my comfort. I forgive
Your sins. Forgive my old man's petulance.
You might have asked me to the ceremony."

Abelard glanced at him: "Do you keep spies?
Our marriage is a secret."
      Fulbert smiled:
"There are no secrets here. So, Heloise,
You come to look at me again?"
        He turned
His face away, and placing chairs where hot
Firelight fell, said: "Tell me of the child."

"A boy," she said. "His name is Astralabe."

"Why Astralabe?"
     Abelard shook his head:
"Why? For the dialing arm that grasps the sun
And makes him in anonymous ocean chart
The mapless."
    "Shall I see him?" said Fulbert.

"He is in Brittany," said Heloise.

"For safety?" Fulbert nodded a dry smile.
"A king you left, a leper you return,
Abelard. Once in anger I foresaw.
Now I am mellower, although I say
You might have asked me to the ceremony —
What is it, friendship? Are you now my nephew?
What do you think that I should do for you?"

"What have I asked?" Abelard answered like
A snapped log spitting streaks.
                              Spreading his palms,
Fulbert said: "You ask nothing. Yet you need.
Your bastions all are down; rosewater days
And nights of nightingales are lost and gone.
Now raucous jackals in your kingdom howl
Holocaust, tattered philosophic troops,
Whom once you limbed and lopped like Hannibal,
Have rallied around Bernard of Clairvaux,
And many a brainless trudger wears your fall
Like Easter in his heart. What will you do?
A bishops' council gathers at Soissons;
And here are you, a wedded heretic,
Whose voice has not been heard in Paris schools
A whole year. Ingrate world, they have forgotten
All but their anger, Peter, and their envy.
What will you do? Give up philosophy,
Buy a fine house and flaunt with Heloise?
Perhaps you should have stayed in Brittany."

Abelard rose and paced away, then turning:
"All that you threatened. You have kept your word,
And do not deprecate your hatred. Fight,
Fulbert, fight. Paris is no paramour
For Bernard. He sniffs halos, fingering
The saintly laurels, orthodox as death,
Imperious and unoriginal
As a king's afterdinner joke. I took
Your challenge. In the morning you shall hear
Me answer it at Mt. Ste. Geneviève."

Fulbert looked startled: "Make me what you will
Monstrous, fling my forgiveness at my head.
But if you speak at Mt. Ste. Geneviève,
You will be stoned."
              Abelard laughed aloud:
"You have done much, but you cannot make Paris
Incurious of words by Abelard.
First they will listen, and then eat their stones."

"The rioters pass hourly," said Fulbert;
"Young firebrains loosed apasture to defend
The truth with sticks. Have you forgotten, Peter?
Your enemies are older than your sins.
Look, too, how criminally you strip your bride
To scorn, if bride she is, married by night
By a bribed bishop to a minorite . . .
Those prayers were gates of peril! She could be
Dragged in the streets by striplings howling whore.
You, if you choose, speak; dance in the flying missiles,

But leave her here with me."
                                    Heloise came
And put her hand in Abelard's. Fulbert
Turned his face toward the fire. From distant streets
Brute throatings barked. Abelard slowly said:
"You praise yourself. I did not come for help;
Only to know if quarrels might have end.
No, I am not compelled to leave her here,
As you think, nor am I afraid to."
                                              "Best,"
Said Fulbert, "not to be afraid. It is
By far more perilous to take her hence."

He looked up evenly at Abelard,
Who feeling Heloise's fingers tremble
Clamped his own hard upon them, leading her
To the low window seat. The whistling croaks
Called nearer from the street's end. Abelard
Smiled bitterly: "Hear them philosophize!
Complacency at least does not unman
This intellectual age!"
                              And as he laughed,
A stone spattered the window into flashing
Meteors, thudded and rolled on the floor.
Fulbert leaped for his servants calling loudly,
But Heloise sat frozen, staring down
At the fierce needles twinkling on her arms
And slippers, glinting eyes of murdered glass
Sewn in her firelit bodice. Abelard
Pulled her beyond the hearthstone. Pounding shouts

Taunted through the torn window; in the hall
The servants waited armed, and over hiss
And seethe, a voice sang arrogantly clear:

> *The heifer and the heretic*
> *Lay rolling in the hayrick,*
> *Libera nos a malo!*
> *Dogma, says he;*
> *Moo, says she;*
> *And in the hay they wallow!*

Abelard ground his teeth, but made no move:
"Tomorrow, these same — "

                              "God's name," Heloise
Cried, "Peter, do not speak tomorrow! Come
Away from Paris, take me away too!
Can you leave me in this house and march off
To martyrdom?"

                   He twisted his lips, saying:
"Our secret should have kept a little longer.
Here might have been your Paris haven. Now
It must be convent walls."

                       And Heloise
Gasping said: "Convent, Peter?"

                         He said: "Patience:
Stone smashed our glass. Nothing. The noise already
Lulls away. Mere students drunk and kicking,
Like many a rout I danced in young myself.
We are not children. In the sober day
My words will load the scale, and fickle heads
Return. Then I will come for you."

                                        He picked
A splinter from her sleeve and gently smoothed
Her shoulder. But her flood of terror broke
In sobs, she crouched to the floor quivering,
And crying "Astralabe." He lifted her,
And Fulbert coming back said: "What? Heloise
Crying? She must stay here. Rocks chase your heels.
You too, of course, tarry until . . . until
Soissons."
            Abelard said impatiently:
"That cloud with its clenched brows over Soissons
Is your millennium. I look to Rome,
Where these provincial nebulosities
Fade in Lateran sunlight."
                                    Fulbert shrugged
Absently, saying: "Your famulus is here,
Arrived among the riot."
                                    Abelard
Frowned opening to Antoine, who shouted, "Master,
I drew blood on the rock thrower. I will do
A penance, but I liked it."
                                    Abelard
Asked: "Have you not deserted? Safety lies
Not in my shadow."
                        "No one has deserted,"
Said Antoine. "These are hurtlings of impatience.
They cannot wait to hear you." He bowed low
To Heloise: "Color your cheeks, madame,
With courage, yes, and pride. I prophesy
Tomorrow crowded halls, and humble tongues."

                            99

"Send off this Delphic famulus," said Fulbert.

"Antoine," said Abelard, "go to the inn,
And hire a horse for me." And Antoine staring,
"Go on," said Abelard; "you will see me
Tomorrow."
        With a sorrowful glance Antoine
Went out. Fulbert said quietly: "A horse,
Peter? I said that you might stay."
        "I heard,"
Said Abelard. "Your hospitality
And pardon stretch to bounds of life itself.
But life must often outlive expectation.
Now, since our vows are criers' matin song,
We shall not crowd your comfort."
        But Fulbert
Pinched his eyes: "Heloise remains with me.
The danger — "
        "Glass is brittle everywhere,"
Said Abelard.
        Fulbert, kicking the stone,
Cried: "What? Is this wedding rice, as your fool
Famulus thinks — "
        "Antoine is not a fool,"
Said Abelard. "Fools reckon absolute
Fixed ends, like you, who sing my dirge tonight.
Tomorrow I may be a festival."

Fulbert said: "I have armed my servants once
Tonight. They still have swords. Depart in peace,

Peter, and travel far. Tomorrow's dawn
Is dark for you. Or stay. It is the same;
But you shall not steal Heloise again."

The settling fire reddened on Fulbert's throat
A silver chain with pendent crucifix,
As if a thread of blood oozed from a wound
And fell in blots. Abelard stared voiceless.
Then Heloise like frost between their eyes
Stood saying: "Uncle, here is not my house.
Your windows are at stake. You risk too much
Playing accomplice to our crime, and panting
To punish it. Be it for concubine
Or wife, or winding sheet, I am Abelard's."

Fulbert's eyes fixed on her like jaws. All three
Stood close and still. Up from the river floated
A drunken voice pealing aloud a song
Of reasonless and scarless merriment,
Then a girl's laughter. On the cobblestones
Outside, a horse was trampling. And Fulbert
Looked down at his own shoes, then at the fire:
"My anger is a fault. I said, forgive.
And yet, you wronged me bitterly."

                                        He sighed:
"So, Heloise, what must I say to you?
You smile now. You were weeping just before.
Woman is woman. I must cry farewell."

He raised his hand and laid it on her hair

I O I

As if to stroke, then pulled it violently
And sent her spinning against Abelard.

"There, take your she philosopher!"
                                    Dark red
In muttering ember light he stood shaking.
Abelard, finding by his hand the mace
Of firetongs, reached, then paused. He flung his arm
Round Heloise, and striding from the room
Found Antoine waiting with a horse below,
A tall fellow who snorted hard and huddled
Them clasped away through the dark chasm of gates.

It was by Argenteuil Abelard paused,
In forests stretching on to convent walls,
Still in auroral dark. He lifted her
From horse and dropped beside her. Heloise
Questionless waited.
                        "There is a spring here,"
He said, and brought her through the trees awhile
Leading the horse, and came to water flowing.
It was too dark to see, the sound was there,
And a low wind in the forest. Heloise
Shivered and drank the water.
                                "We are near,"
Said Abelard. "The convent will have wine."
They rested by the water saying nothing,
While the great hands of light began to feel
Their way in the woods. Then Heloise:
                                    "How near?

Where is the convent where I wait for you?
It makes no difference."
                              "Argenteuil," he said.
"I will come soon. The sisters will be kind."

The forest shook with chills of the dawn wind.
Heloise said nothing, while he took her hands,
And watched the grey fire brighten on her face.
"Heloise," he said. She only looked at him.
"Heloise, never look for us again
Beyond this hour, unless I teach aloud
The lands of birth and love."
                              She did not answer,
Nor even smile. The brightness of the sky
Silvered the water like a leaping fish.
The horse drove his foot into the wet sod.

"It is dawn," said Abelard; she rose and followed
Back to the road. They mounted and rode down
A little hill to Argenteuil, stopping
By the white convent as the sun came up.

"Here is the peace you asked," he said to her.
"I grant it to you for a little while.
Pray that my thoughts may be of polished lightning,
Pray, and then sleep."
                              She raised her face to his,
But the door opened, and the Prioress
Appeared.
              "Mother," he said, "we cry to you

Asylum. Here is money for the poor.
I shall come back for her."
                              The Prioress
Bowed her head: "Is it Heloise? Yes, yes,
God turns His face again toward penitence."

"I shall come back for her," said Abelard
Again. The Prioress nodded and went in.
Heloise paused on the top stair and turned
To Abelard as he mounted.
                              "Very soon,"
He said and smiled at her. She shook her head,
And the horse wheeled away and matins rang.

The lifting brow of sunlight as he rode
Tormented him to drowse; pommel and mane
Kept wakeful rhythm, and the brooks flashed by
Bright blue, the forest shook with wings. One cloud,
Heavy with loads of thunder like a cart,
Rolled up the sky, and suddenly its lash
Fell on a towering tree, which burned alive
Immortalized. Abelard spurred his horse,
And as the shower dissolved, by Paris gates
Dismounted, and climbed pondering word on word,
Word upon step, up words and streets of stairs,
Climbed word by stair, by morning bells, to where
Antoine was waiting on Mt. Ste. Geneviève.
"Master," he said, "the sun that shines on you
Has warmed the hungry hundreds from their beds
To hear. What did I say? Your world is whole."

He opened the doors wide. In sunlit hush,
Abelard saw the faces turned to him.
He smiled a little at Antoine, then settling
His gown, mounted his lectern and began.
He spoke, and they were silent till he ended,
And in the silence as he closed his book,
He stood a moment; and then turned, and walked
Through hurricanes of shouts and clattering hands
Numbing his ears, throats tossing up his name
Victoriously, feet stamping jubilee.
Antoine received him dancing.

                    "Yes, Antoine,"
Said Abelard, "this philosophic mob
Approves my demagoguery. Remember
The bishops at Soissons, remember Bernard —
Half saint, not half philosopher enough.
Saints fix their eyes above us, and like beasts
Fight for the power of victory with claws
Unmatched by reason. Blessed are the poor
Of intellect, for they shall be canonized.
Bernard and Fulbert . . . I am exhausted. Go,
Go let me sleep. Go, heathen. Let me sleep."

Antoine went down the hill into the sun
Of afternoon. Abelard was alone.
There lay the city, and the miles of river
Hammered by the sun crawled silverly to sea.
Where white streams of the forest are dawnlit,
Over the world the matin bells are ringing
Messages and messages, like larks in lofts

Of morning in the perishing night. He turned
And climbed to his old chamber, and there found
The dust heavy, the gold light falling softly
On the benign old volumes, on the inkstand,
Passing through windowpanes mysteriously
With an old look . . . messages, messages.
Abelard fell on the bed and was asleep
Before he had divined those messages,
And through his sleep a matin bell was ringing
Silver, a hundred miles up in the air,
A tiny hammer falling on it clearly,
And the hand holding it and striking it
Faded upward invisible, as the forest
Brought darkness rolling up across the sky,
Dream in the leaf mold died, and hours passed . . .

Until the silk of sleep was torn with fire.

Not dreaming, but aware of the red flame,
He fought air with his hand, and woke himself.
"Come," said Fulbert, "the Master is awake."
He gave his torch to a dark faced fellow,
And came close to the bed: "How do you feel,
Peter? I heard that you were gravely ill."

Abelard stretched his hands behind his head,
Looking from face to face: "Why do you bring
This army of bituminous looking dogs?"

Fulbert said lightly: "You are discourteous,

But you are not yourself. You are diseased."

Abelard slid his hand under his pillow,
But found no weapon. He smiled evenly,
Glancing from belt to belt. "I must be sick,"
He said, "to leave my door unlocked. Or have you
A key?"
       Fulbert said smiling: "There are keys
Of privacy and keys of mastery —
Even as words are power, that should be pledge.
Your intellect commands . . . God only can
Define you, Abelard. My poor opinion
Is mortal, untrimmed by philosophy."

"God will perhaps define me at Soissons,"
Said Abelard; "impatience is a fault.
Philosophy nails dialectic thwarts
From brink to brink of man's uncertainties,
And in the end might even define you,
Fulbert. Rules in the end control me, rules
Unknown to you, but rules."
       Fulbert shot out
His finger furiously: "You have no rules.
You are a voice of sirens on the reef.
You sing and all men listen. All save I,
Who keep the key to lock Satan in hell.
Where have you taken her?"
       "She is my wife,"
Said Abelard. And Fulbert, "Yes, your wife,
By night, by a bribed bishop, in the crypt

Of Notre Dame. You think that you can have
All things, and on your own conditions."

"Yes,"
Said Abelard, and his voice sharply rose
In anger and contempt, "I make conditions
For what is mine."

"Then you have made this too,"
Fulbert said, leaning his face over him.
Abelard twisting to one side a little
Edged toward the nearest belt, where a long knife
Hung glittering.

"Yes, you have made conditions;
Full cause I grant you, Abelard, for all
Done past, and done tonight. I scorn your death.
Death is for men. For goats and gargoyles, laughter.
Now I can see you whole, philosopher,
Thief, whoremaker, whoremonger . . ."

"Fool," said Abelard
Between his teeth, and snatched the dagger, jumped,
Struck left and right, and blood fell on the floor.
He came to Fulbert. "Fool," he said, and raised
The dagger, but they pinned him from behind,
And Fulbert laughed:

"The Master has gone mad,
And needs a surgeon. Madness, a disease
Of manhood, an impurity. Come surgeon,
Purify, purify."

They held him fast,
While one carved out his madness with a knife.

X

Under the cliff the sea sleeps,
  Under the cliff the bird swings
On hollowed wing, sheltered in shadow,
  By crevice of cool rock covered, hovers
                    and sings.

At Argenteuil the shadows pierce
  From the rocks of the wall, from
                    crumbling mortar,
Shadow and crying of sea birds
  Over farewell water.

She, pierced and overdraped with the dark
  Of Argenteuil, had waited long;
No second coming of Abelard
  Would crack the night she lay among.

He had come once, ill and shrunken,
  To tell what she must know,
And grafted shadows deep upon her,
  And made them grow.

He stretched their shame upon her arms,
  Making remission for her grace,
And bitterly had he departed;

And Heloise, lying upon her face
Alone in her cell, and after many years,
But not so many years that she was dead
Or shrunk into the shadows of the convent,
Or felt no longer a firm breast rising
Hopelessly under black — Heloise, face down
In broken sleep, lay dreaming hastily
   How she no longer lay in her gown,
   But ran naked, cold and naked,
   Over dead leaves, over brown,
   Running, running a hundred years.
   Breath came sorrowfully through her mouth,
   Dead trees flickered by like spears
   Of haggard armies put to rout.
   A dim fire fled like a galaxy
   Far down the avenue of trees,
   Faint lantern burning redly, fainter,
   Fainter always, and Heloise
   Through the dead leaves ran, and stopped at last;
   Dead trees went on in an endless row;
   She said: "You run as far and fast
   For a moment past as a year ago."

   She had run far from every track,
   But heard a bell ring from a tower,
   And wandering, without the power
   To know if she were going back
   Or onward, or forever on,
   She stood before the convent door

And found she had a visitor;
And she awoke and found it was Antoine.

They sat in the lamplight with the Prioress near.
"I have not seen him," said Antoine. "I know
This only: he has built a hermitage,
The Paraclete, he names it; there he lives,
The man of glory beached, a ship borne inland
By hurricane, and planted in the soil."

She said: "He planted darkness in me too.
God's nun I seem, but I am Abelard's,
Dead for his sake, who could have lived for him.
I am not angry, Antoine. I am dead."

Antoine said: "But our life is not so fragile.
You sleep still. I received a letter from him."

Her eyes opened like a young girl's; Antoine
Smiling a little sorrowfully said:
"But it was not for me; it was for you.
I brought it to you."
                                Heloise' eyes fell.
Then he gave her the letter and stood up;
And since she still said nothing, went away.
When Heloise had read those grievous lines,
It was deep night. She fell back on her couch,
And lay with clear eyes open staring upward.
Exhausted beyond sleep, empty at last

Of thought, she stretched her silence out threadbare
Against gigantic silences, and heard
From the pressed clouds, from waters over the earth,
Soft thunderings of the wide living world.

Past midnight, she could hear the sound of water:
Down every hillside under the forest, white sprang the
                                        arching foam,
It flushed dark roots and smothered a million stones,
It slipped like eels through the coiling and smooth raceways
                                        of the worn rock,
And spun in a thousand basins. Then came the rivers,
Presumptuous, shouldering their portly way seaward,
Nudging their banks aside. At last the sea,
A dimpled grey fastness, bearing frankly under the sky
                                        its broad surface,
Footing the heavenhigh pillars of the rain.
So lay the fathoms once over the whole earth, when silence
Became the voice of the living and dead, and the thin
                                        white lips
Of breaking waves licked only the timber line of
                                        Mount Ararat,
Before the conceiving again of mountains.

She suddenly felt rain all round her cell,
A single downward forest from one seed;
Rain going down the naked branch and lightly
Jingling in gutter leads by convent walls.
She lay and listened, for it had a voice,
And might have words; but now, straining to sift

The rain's quick dunning blur, she could not hear,
For her tears beat so fast and angrily
Their hot way down her face, her listening broke
And she lay choking, scalding in her throat,
Making her fingers talons at the sheet.
And far away God thoughtfully in heaven
Sat high between mysterious Cherubim,
His left hand idly stirring pools of cloud,
Shaking rain steadily on the convent roof.
And drumming at the walls it turned to words,
Singing distinct autumnal music, cold
Grace of three voices' hollow harmony:

Rain:
My unending merciful
Downward beat and upward pull
Balance all things visible.
Sleep again and twist the wool
Over eyes and over hair;
Moistening downward, falling dull,
I, unending merciful,
Down the forest, down the wall,
Down the double church tower fall,
Down the quenched and birdless air.
Living mouths unknowable
Whisper up each listening lull,
Like the spinning of a spool,
Hastening, vast, and musical.
We are scholars of one school,
Many, many, dropping null,

Dropping globular, pock the pool.
Hear the echo of the skull,
Hear the lives untraceable,
Hear the grass innumerable,
Hear the rivers filling full,
Hear the forest wet and full,
Hear the ocean more than full,
Merciful, merciful . . .

The rain sang on, but now another voice
Made four, aged and yearning, as though chained
To dungeons of sensation and desire
Through winter centuries:

Earth:
                    I underlie.
Hundreds of hidden wombs huddled in me
Send up the summer. Weak
And faint I lie, when spring suns making free
Kiss mouth and cheek.
                    I underspeak.
The granite lies too heavy on the shale.
Then restless, I
Heave my hips and rock foundations fail,
Bricks fly.
I swing my shoulders free of monuments.
What if the undermurmurer repents
Her Atlas bargain? If I only breathe,
Like serpents shall the hedgerows coil and seethe

And treetops totter down like falling fountains.
Shall I shout under and unpile the mountains?
The word is all I seek.

Silence lulled, and two children's throats began
A summery song, almost too high to hear:

> Air:
> I lie in a clear ring
> And make myself a drape
> Around each visible thing
> That gives me shape.
> I fashion all things young and old,
> And my impalpable hands mold
> And camber the immortal sky.
> I chisel out the lily bloom,
> I file the grass and blur the fly,
> Sculpturing to fit its fatal room
> Your flesh, till in the wrench of storm
> All is shattered except form.
> For I am circle, angle, square,
> Rhomboid, trapezoid, I am air;
> Trodden by light, treading in turn
> The shapes of the world like fossil fern,
> Till the prints lie deeply carven in
> The white facet of my skin.

Heloise drew her breath; the air blew back,
And down the cavern rolled a burning star.

Star:
    We must shout to each other.
My voice rings like fire that tears through brass.
The blast furnace of Beta, my golden brother,
    Gleams like boiling glass.
But now I hear no longer; his voice dies
    Midway sidereal winds,
As orbits swing out into broader skies.
    So of love, God rescinds
All but the flashing points that meet your eyes.
    I draw my burial gown
About, I burn myself to the last bone.
The great coffin of darkness is nailed down
    On me, inside alone.

"Let all unlive itself," she answered him,
"Rain, star, and earthquake, air and Heloise.
And where we made ourselves or lost ourselves,
Where our tracks lie, though many a
                                wimpled morning
Illumine them, while by the tentacles
Of earth death holds us pure and undisturbed,
Trouble us not with afterstrength. Let pass,
Let be."
                All voices stilled, she was alone.

Not under the curved cell roof, but under the cell
Of the curved and falling sky, Heloise stood,
The wet of the grass underfoot, her face
Brushing the tops of the rain. Tall as the rain,

She stood, gazing down the white cliff of her body
Upon a carven map. Her feet were lost
Among the woods of France, and with her right hand
She reached and stroked the shoulder of
                              Mont Blanc;
Snow shuddered from her touch, fluttered and flung
A light fog sinking over Chamonix.
She watched it falling, and as her foot stirred
A second avalanche combed off and fell.
Should she unpile the mountains? A far warmth
Reached her, and the rain sank, and began falling
Only from her limp hands and ends of hair.
She looked, and a giant pinwheel star came spouting
Hissing, and scarped a red arc round her head,
Spattering shards and flakes of itself beyond
Far into echoing cubic miles of black.
Her foot began to climb a blade of grass,
Sliding easily up the moist green stem
And off the tip to nowhere. The last rain
Blew from her skirt, the star had bored a hole
And buried itself, no mountains stood out here,
And the air ended; and she closed her eyes
Not knowing where she leaped. There was no where,
Only a lapping by of little waves
Of atom stuff, no noise, not one wave broke,
As face-down over all she was among
She drifted for another hundred years,
And for another hundred years she drifted
Among all that her hair filtered and breathed,
While round her motionless hands and shuttered eyes,

The night was ending, and the immobile dark
Became tomorrow.

        By the withered light
Which bore today, she saw her sleeping hands.
The night had opened, and the rain was gone.
Bright from the east wall of the yielding earth,
The morning wreaks itself on tower and tree,
On moving rivers and on convent walls,
Shouting in meteors from mouth to mouth,
Whispering in lift of air, in drifting fall
Of sea, in rifted soil. Lithe and waking
Its answer tramps on flooding silences.
Over the east wall the stretched arm of morning
Lies whitening from bone out through the flesh,
Then sweeps downward and gathers up the valleys,
And hoards the mountains and the cataracts.
It counts the cities with its gold forefinger
And lays them back in order where they lie,
And piling the Alps again, and storming westward,
Blowing back flashing tides from Finisterre,
Plunges on to the rough gray cobblestoned
Atlantic, and the nameless coil of seas.

XI

With the new year, when like a slackening spring
The ecliptic trails its planets westerly,
Past perihelion light with streaming sail,
Earth, like a tall ship slanting in the wash,
Her frozen bows champing the soft ether,
Sweeps wakeless round, and turns to beat upwind
To the spring buoy of the solar year.
Beneath her bows the gibberish tongue of time
Ripples and riddles, and strange constellations,
Helmeted with fire, stalk blazing through the dark
On wintervested continents of space.
Skillful in bitterness the midnight watch;
Dumb and remote the tongues of hourly things.

The fragile hermitage called Paraclete,
Carelessly built by Abelard in summer,
Sang like a false harp in the winter wind.
The frost wrote Chinese on the window pane,
And Abelard, abandoning the lines
In a known language, read the unknown tongue.
Blurred by those white ideographs, the moon
High risen over the forest foamed and seethed
Beyond the window; naked and shining danced
The many armed forest against the sky.

What language is it written in?
Latin, the language of the Church.
What language is it written in?
Latin, she speaks a dainty Latin . . .
What language is it written in?

                                He stared
Again at her letter; language of Heloise.
He saw the pale hair falling by her shoulder,
He saw her foot climbing a blade of grass,
He saw the avalanche of ponderous snows
Tear off Mont Blanc and race over the glaciers.
Where had she written those words? He searched
                              in vain
To find them; we must shout to one another,
My voice rings . . . He could not quite remember,
Yet it was wonderfully merciful.

  Night quenched, the light of the sky,
  Night quenched, the birdless light
  Hovers and springs and answers . . . where?
It was all wonderfully merciful
How all the waters of the world descend,
How all the mountains of the world arise.
  Who shouts below, who shouts on high?
  Who tears the forest in passing spite?
  Who shapes the sun, who molds the air?

He read her words again, the moon moved fast
And raced across the sky; the daylight came.

Antoine shivering in the winter morning

Knocked loudly at the door of the Paraclete,
And roused Abelard.

          "Merciful God," he said,
And drew the boy inside, grasping his body
Like the first heat of grace in absolution.

"Master," said Antoine, "here is room for two men.
Let it have two."
         But Abelard, unclasping
His arms: "You are too large. This hermitage
Is small, and houses only a half a man."

"What is a man?" asked Antoine.
            "Quiet, boy,"
Said Abelard. "Glory and time are gone."

Antoine said: "Then the timeless in the dark."

Abelard shook his head: "What am I now?"

"Asleep," said Antoine; "waking is within.
Why am I here — no self within yourself —
Except that I have been to Argenteuil,
And seen her . . ."
        "Yes," said Abelard, "and shown
My letter to her. You are much to blame.
Have you come here to speak of Heloise?
If so, then you forget. For I am past
Being moved by woman."
        "I forget nothing. You

Forget," said Antoine. "Why did you write to me?
And why should I not go to Argenteuil?
Heloise was not angry. She perceived
How masterless by moonset, by this dim
Interlunation, while you burrow here,
The children of your intellect must hide
Or hasten, do like derelicts, and hunt
The currents of the great sea's whorl coiling
Slow to the unmoved center. Is it here,
Abelard? Is this the core? Is this cold staring
Grimace of desolation the world's heart?"

"What did she say to you?" said Abelard.

"A nun for Abelard, but not for God,
She called herself; as if not love, but envy
Had dressed her in the bridal black of Christ.
She is the same, as you would recognize
If you heard one word from her."

                                        "I have heard,"
Said Abelard, then staring at the floor
Sat voiceless . . . Wonderfully merciful
How all the waters shout to one another . . .
At last repeated softly: "I have heard.
She is the same. What struggle was it? What
Heart hacking ingenuity of rage!
And there is nothing left but the same two
With miles and vows between, and penitence.
What we could never see now sees us clearly.
While Paris knew our secret, suavely sinning

Among all eyes, we never saw the angel's;
Now through the chinked roof glares the demon star.
Where is the peace of God? A frivolous name
Bestowed on sins well buried in the mob,
Where no eye sees the angel eye askance
On bright crusades, fur, kisses, crosses, laughter.
It is not here, not in the house of God
Where the eye steadily stares down to bone,
Down through bone to corrupt soft marrow guilt.
My penitence, my blame! Here I repent,
While the world rocks and shudders on its axles,
Cart of the doomed. Echoes of Hell boil up;
Howls of the down-there damned, cremated living
On the deep griddle floor, offend my hymn
Of liar's penitence! Here I betray
Power of my passion, calling it sin, praying
For peace! And I learn nothing. The thief steals,
Repents; the bishop fornicates, repents.
And I repent, with hatred of God gasping
In all my veins for vengeance. Oh, the angel,
Antoine, the angel!"
                        He flung up his head,
And calmed his voice: "Go home, Antoine; go now.
The Paraclete is a true hermitage,
Where one man is alone."
                        Antoine in silence
Arose and touched the door: "The masterless,"
He said, "need have no fear of heresy.
The benediction of your steel gray word
Awaits its listeners. Lap us in arms

Of lead, to sink by rules."
                            But Abelard
Bitterly muttered: "Rules, there are no rules."

Then Antoine said again: "You are asleep,
But waking is within. Unruled the sleeper
Loves and speaks. Your school shall come to you.
And if you will, you can send us away,
And if you must, you will invent the words."

Antoine went out, and Abelard was alone,
While the long fingered clock of suns and moons
Opened and shut gigantic senseless eyes,
Timing and altering unhurriedly
Adam's primeval names, outdistancing
The summers of surrender and the sheen
Of morning victories, where after years
The gray wall crumbles and uncountable
Flowers revive dominion. Adam could not
Make names for everything, for horned fish
Feathering to crested bird, vestigial wing,
Leg rudiment, mute gland. Who could foresee
In each cell's hoop, wheeled by a striding hour
Destinied black, the laughter on the bright
Hour's face, the sun's gold irony, as all
Turn opposite, till the nightmare-knowing brain
Floats under skull like the wind's winding sheet?
From wilderness the shouting cities rise
And towers totter back to wilderness;
The nakedness of flowers can be clothes

For heathendom, while weedy saints fly up
Frockless of all but heavenly fire. The hour
Whips all the nameless circles by, driving
New hands to drum on aging doors, turning
Death's hermitages into living schools.

Abelard looked at the new huts arising,
Circling his own among the chilly woods,
And said to Antoine: "I can think of nothing
Proper to eagerness. In those young eyes,
I read my sunk meridian. This work
Is yours, not mine."
                              And Antoine, with his hand
In mortar where he reared his walls, his face
Pinched white with hungering frost, answered:
                                        "Perhaps
The words are still to come. But do your will,
Send us away. There are no rules."
                                        And turning
Back to his half built house he squared a stone
In place, and set another on its head.

And Abelard sent none away, but waited
While the long bladed axe of hours went on
Chipping the winter days away, until
An icy morning when he found himself
Before a circle of their books and eyes,
And wondering if he had willed these words:

"My text, the praise of eunuchs. Hear me out.

I did not haul you here, you came yourselves
Hunting out answers from philosophy.
Where something died and rotted, where a sick
White life crawls and perpetuates itself
In buried blackness or unpitying sun,
The worms of knowledge gnaw. The worms that dined
On Aristotle taught him most at last.
Had he been eaten of worms before he died,
Like the bad Tetrarch, or like me, his knowledge
Would not have been an Organon, but fire
Spiraling out of every twisted instant,
Fire of the crematorium, hell fire.
Consider then the love of Origen,
Who struck away his twin globes of desire
That he might burn one pillar of desire.
He knew the mighty mother of the hills,
The padding of her lion's paw, the bang
Of her imperial cymbals. Sapling minds
Lack sacrifice. You come without confession,
Dreaming a Caesar's monolith, so taking
Knowledge to the damnation of your souls.
What can I teach, save hell's ambiguous
Elixir? Will you learn? Then cut away
Your logic, simple tokens, daisies, rings,
And come into communion. We dwell far
From Paris schools, from lizards on the rock
Painting their skin to any lichen color.
White is the color of the Paraclete,
The snow that silts down through the cloven thatch
White doves of the word's bursting eloquence.

If you are cold, turn home; but if cold wind
Alone consoles your flesh, hear, and rejoice."

The scholars heard in silence and remained.
But later by the dozing lamp, Antoine
Said: "There is a sermon to lift echoes winging
Like scared birds from Clairvaux."

                                    And Abelard:
"The holy abbot will not long neglect us.
After Soissons, I had him in my dreams
Nightly, clipping a quill to grave my doom,
Scribbling in his close cell below the stairs.
Even now he works, gray eyes and gentle hands,
The flickerless inexorable candle
Glazing his features, gleaming lucent rose
Through the thin, pale pendentive of his nostrils.
And on my inner lids I read his words:
'Bernard of Clairvaux to his Holiness:
The Church can have no peace with Abelard,
Poor mangled wretch, on whom the devil early
Set hoof, a eunuch serving at God's altar,
Which Scripture forbids flat, a heretic
Trisecting the high Trinity with reason,
Tearing from the gray gown of Christendom
The cross betokening her holy war . . .'
Oh, the denunciation will come soon,
The pen will soon be scratching, dipping, scratching,
The seal will stamp upon the clotted wax.
Tomorrow or the next day it will come."
Antoine said: "But the thunder of Soissons

Waits leashed in the Pope's silence. Your appeal
Folds like the triple wings of an archangel
Around you."
                    Abelard with a slow smile
Murmured: "Small choice for Innocent between
The hand that set tiaras on his head
And me here, muttering in the wilderness
Wizardries to a college of no rule!
And you too all must suffer; the next council
Will blow the last trump of authority."

"Is hell alone," said Antoine suddenly,
"A haven for the good?"
                    Then Abelard
Spoke almost merrily: "Hell is the silence
Tending the shrunken deathbed of desire.
I loved once, but now no passion will gnaw
Except at my own bone, while hung with years
Will sags to willingness. Only the saints
Stab without question and with eyes fast shut,
Who lulled by evensongs of Augustine,
And roused by matin lions of Jerome,
Have kissed authority like children. Oh,
Farewell, my loss! Love is the scorpion fenced
With fire, and so, the ninth hour, the rent veil,
And every cold and bloodstained tree that ever
In leafless shame stretched out God's yearning arms!
Hell triples heat from hour to hour, quickening
The soul warm and awake. Out of Clairvaux,
A cooling wind may blow some back to heaven."

But the days passed, the snow shrank, and the sun
Sped through his equinox. His climbing stature
Reached for the solstice, and still Abelard
Lectured to pilgrim boys, priests, scholars, minstrels,
And no wind from Clairvaux, while summer bloomed
And aged. The woods around the Paraclete
Had bronzed their mosses with flame crippled leaves
Before the stamp of hoofs and thud of boots
Dismounting told the changing of the season.
Abelard heard, and rose from where he sat
Expounding, in late sun where wind was still,
And saw a youthful cardinal, elegant
In ruddy plumage, bearing in one hand
A letter; on the other listlessly
He turned the seal ring of Pope Innocent.
Three beadles and a brother of Clairvaux
Stood with him, their hands stifled in their sleeves.
Abelard bowed:
              "I have been waiting here
Some days for you."
                  The cardinal gently smiled:
"The antipapacy has clogged our streams.
I bring a letter."
              Abelard wearily
Said: "But forbear the words; I know them all.
Say only where the next council will be."

"At Sens," the cardinal said. "Instruct yourself
In patience; for unless you hear the letter,
Our holy process cannot be fulfilled.

We carry nails and hammers, and must peg
Your doors to silence."
                    "Read," said Abelard.
And while the scholars gathered silently,
The cardinal read, and when he finished, handed
The scroll to Abelard, who said:
                              "I see
The name and heraldry of Innocent,
But Bernard wrote the Latin, as I thought."

The cardinal murmured: "At the Pope's request
He did so. He obeys as I obey."

Abelard laughed aloud: "Now cry the tongues
Of Pentecost! Now I shall obey you,
As you obey the abbot of Clairvaux
Who in his turn obeys his pawn at Rome.
Our serpent language bites his tail at last,
And so the contest of Soissons is done,
And heresy transfixed. Yet we must play
It all again, at Sens."
                    The cardinal shrugged
With a pained smile: "I carry no instructions
Beyond God's will as herein written down.
The letter is quite absolute and clear:
These must disperse at once. As for yourself,
You are a hermit and this house your own;
You may dispose your leisure till you come
To Sens."
              He sighed and added: "Heresy

Confuses me. I do not know why reason
Cannot trisect the Trinity. Perhaps
It can."

      "Come, nail the doors," said Abelard;
"But not my door, for it is mine."

                And Antoine:
"Mine also; I will risk the consequence."

The cardinal glanced around: "Speak to your friends,
Abelard. Wasted courage troubles me,
And the Pope is not trifling."

             Abelard
Raising his brows said: "Nor am I; and yet,
I know a stricken field."

         He turned gravely
On the rebellious faces: "Save yourselves.
A wasted courage cuts memorials,
But cut them for yourselves and not for me.
Go, I forbid resistance. Nails and words
Are incommensurate. I will not have
My pupils fall into such fallacy
As blinds the Pope. The council shall decide."

They stood silent a while, then slowly moved
Past Abelard, touching his hand farewell.
Only Antoine stood looking at the sky.
"Antoine?" said Abelard.

         Antoine sat down
Quietly on the ground. The cardinal shrugged
And sighed again. "Hammer," said Abelard.

Then the woods rang the echo of their pounding
A long hour, till crossed wooden barriers
In rows forbade the doors to speak, above
The skulls of leaves. And scattering masterless
The scholars trundled books and gowns away;
Till about nightfall the Pope's emissary
Bidding farewell departed, and the night
Came silently to the unpeopled doors
And smokeless chimneys round the Paraclete.
Only one lamp, where Antoine reading late
Still sat, burned neighborly till midnight, then
Blew out, and Abelard was left alone.

XII

Alone in the cold Paraclete he sat
Reading her letter. Formless wind through walls
Whimpering shaped of lintel, door and lamp
Barrows of the far flying air, beneath
Whose definition raged the naked tree.
Reading and reading he sat still, reading
And reading. How had she found her multitude
Of words? He read the ligatures of veins
In leaves, of sun in crevices of bark;
He read the last whisper of dying men,
And the child's mystery of poolbent sticks;
He heard the swan speak and the stone remember.
He saw the cold rain falling, cold and careless,
Thrusting and pulling, wounding earth, while days
Decayed and dawned. He read it as if written,
How angels shred their wings in flight, hearing
Tumble and whirr, humanity's unmaking;
Hundreds of cataracts' descending power,
Hundreds of hidden wombs' travailing summer;
More things becoming than could dream of being,
And Adam needing time to name it all.

Abelard whispered, fingering her words:
"In darkening glades, love weariless, love,

Still stalking prints of memory's wild deer,
Becomes itself the hunted, pierced with arrows,
Betrayed, caught in the womb and cataract,
In penitence, in time and season, pod
Of living seed, and death's slow spreading stain.
Let angels flee. Among the water reeds
Winds mourn the myth of leaves, the phantom flowers
Lost, lost. One sunrise and the lovely hair
Blows wide in the wind; seed of the dandelion
Blows wide away; still gracious the young knee
Sinks in the dug soil. Slippery the wheel turns,
Turning down glossy heads. Is God appeased?
Who is He, whom I named upon that early
Kiss, when I said, Now all I know is real?
Was God then the mere moisture of my tongue
That when I spoke I used His language only?
Was God, whose morning stars all sang together,
My caged domestic lark singing for me?
I cannot see. With the descending leaf
My hand is joined, yet I become nothing,
Fertilize nothing, prizeless and unprized,
A winter wraith, unman . . ."
                                        And Abelard
Plunging his face in his hands cried: "Where
                                        is death?"

Far into aging night he wept alone,
Pressing his eyeballs, till like painted glass
Refractions spattered in the dancing dark,
Rolling his head upon the rock of knuckles,

And his lips murmuring against her letter:
"When will the ink of Judgment Day be dry?
The scribe still toils, the book is never done.
The angel of its meaning, drop by drop,
Distilled in frigid names falls, strained through time.
Late and stillborn are all the names of knowledge;
But this lone draughty mansion betrays love
To a hard point alone in the huge night,
Meaning unlearned, unlearning, white with anguish,
Desire stripped objectless . . . Impenitent
Of names and knowledge, stone that swims on air,
Fire quenching rain . . . What can God say?
                                His torrent
Of will is dammed to a still pool, who willed
Earth breed and bear, and He devour the child
Newborn, He violent philanderer
Hugging the harbor of the womby world,
Breeding and swallowing. What can He do
But rage, and send down rain to bleak its light,
Wonderfully merciful, in loops of change?
He is a cold rain falling on the soil,
A changeless rain, whose waters like the sea
Flowerless breed a solitary flower,
Stern blossom of belief. Yes, God is mine,
Yet if I build Him out of changeless rain,
When I have built, He will be changeless rain,
And all I know of Him will still be tears.
And if I build Him out of changeless love,
When I have built, He will be changeless love,
And all I know of Him still Heloise.

And she will die, and He who cannot die
Waits in the cemetery of my brain
Carved in His self's invisible white stone,
Whose epitaph is written, deep and ruddy
Bloodwrought uncials eating into marble:
Love, loss; belief, betrayal; desire, death.
A changeless rain. And He will wash away
Even these written words which are Himself.
Yes, God will wash even Himself away."

Night plunging into seasonless dimensions
Of black moonset, unquarried stars, playing
On toothed edges of chaos and curved rims
Of cloud, put out all clocks and ticking thoughts
In sleep. He lay, his face upon her words,
On the bare table, by the lamp whose pallor
Doubled the coming dawn; and saw a dream:
A space of wind and waters,
Clouds slashed with heavy swords of light, the steaming
Tumble of early earth, cataracts
Trumpeting into glens of fern and fury, avalanche
Hurtling the raked cliffs gobbling downward, flamed darts of
                                striping meteors
Vaunting and volleying whiplashes of fire.
And through all a woman's voice, dolorously lamenting
For births in vain; the wrath of iron thewed Earth Mother
                                clashing
Summons to sons unslain yet, groaned for vengeance
On Heaven, lordly wounder of wombs:
"Children arise, avenge me on your father

Who makes my labor issueless!"
                              Terror kept silence,
Blasphemy echoing responseless, till from the
                              barrows boomed
Of the dark a bold voice: "Dastard father despising,
I will avenge issueless labor."
                              Laughing the Earth
Mammoth mother rejoiced in the word, and mightily
Ambushed her champion, child of a crafty hour,
Armed his hand with the whitetoothed hook of a scythe,
Counseled him cunning to wait and work.
Leading on then the night in lust came giant Heaven
And in fume and in fire fell hotly round Earth, hungering
And holding, heaving himself all round her body;
Out of the ambush hurled the champion charging,
Seized, whirled the whitetoothed scythe, shearing
The Heaven's manhood off, and flung it away,
Behind him, down. Yet drops of that blood, not
                              vainly fallen,
Earth caught, conceiving; and in circling years
Bore multitudes of darkness, murderous
Gigantic shapes, gleaming in arms, and shivering horror,
And shadowy fleeing phantoms too, night wandering
Dream featured nymphs, with grace of ash trees growing
On mountain slopes.
                    But the parts plundered, slashed
                              with steel,
Dropped on the wet pulse of the grizzled sea;
And the sea carried them an endless age,
White foam flushing round the immortal flesh,

And in the foam the flowerless harvestless
Ocean conceived a flower, harvest of salt
Waste wandering, a maidenly divine
Damsel, who naked shapely setting foot
Blossomed the bare sand shore with petal pride,
Gold burgeonings of fecund love arising
And carpeting uphill round Cythera's
Rock breasts; and in the sky above her head,
Lanced by the low sun, edged with rainbow rose,
A silver coronet of cloud appeared . . .
Close then she came before his sleeping eyes,
And called: "Rise, answer. Do I seem to you
The same as once you knew me long ago?"

Under the dazzling dream the sleeper tossed
His fallen head: "The face of deity
Is death. Let me not live unmanned, strengthless
In scorn."
      And she serenely, fading slowly:
"Chain to your mind's wall fast in solitude
This memory. You cannot tell my face
To friend or future. Silence is my name
But lightning is its voice. Beware. Be still."

And Abelard awoke to the wide day.

On his cold window early frost had built
Ice cryptograms; but at the forest's edge,
Late starlings, glossing their dark wings with dawn,
Haggled in the frail sun harsh hymns, midarctic

Latin. Abelard raised his head, and found
His pen, and wrote to her of penitence,
Blessing her nunnery, and sealed and sent.

Eleven days he waited. On the twelfth
Before his door the messenger from Sens
Sounded the trumpet of farewell. Antoine
And Abelard, in a red autumn twilight,
Stood in sloughed leaves. Antoine had nailed the door.

"Which way?" said Antoine.
                    "All the way," he answered.

Antoine glanced gravely at the sky, and said
Again: "The mad wind pours. Which way?"
                              "Antoine,"
Said Abelard, "You have another name
You never told me. Keep it secret still.
A name in secret is a unicorn
Who purifies the waters of the world."

"Where shall I seek the waters?" asked Antoine.

And Abelard: "You came from Italy.
You must go back to Italy, where I
Myself would go, except I go to Sens."

Smiling unhappily Antoine murmured:
"Shall I find you again?"
                    But Abelard:

"How can I tell? God has his future, I
Have mine. In Rome, greet Innocent for me."

The night wind blew a long tide up the forest,
Rolling a wild flotsam of leaves.
                              "Goodnight,
Antoine!" said Abelard. He turned and went
Northward into the forest and the wind.
But Antoine waited in the dark alone
All night, crouched at the Paraclete's low stair.
When it was gray, he stood up stiff and cold,
And there was nothing but a little house,
A shipwreck of the wind in a great sea
Of drifted leaves, and no bell in the tower.
He turned away, and southward with the wind
Blew down the long road into Italy.